FIGHTING COCKPITS
1914–2000

FIGHTING COCKPITS
1914–2000

Design and development of military aircraft cockpits

L.F.E. Coombs

Airlife
England

Acknowledgements

Encouragement for writing this book came from many friends in avionics, ergonomics and aviation history. Valuable assistance with information and illustrations came from the aerospace industry and these are listed.

In particular I must express my appreciation of the advice given so willingly: by Robert Haslam and Martin Evans of British Aerospace and Harrier test pilot John Farley: by Roger FitzPatrick and Nick H. Fox of Smiths Industries, by Bill Gunston and by Mike Hirst of BAe/Loughborough University Intl Educational Centre who read an early draft and provided valuable guidance on the contents: by B.E.R. Ballard who checked much of the final version and Ted Hooton, who advised on the captions for Mosquito radar equipment, and Derek James who advised on the technical level: by R.R. Johnstone and John Smith on the history of HUD technology: by Richard Riding and Mike Oakey of *Aeroplane Monthly* who, as usual, were most helpful in providing illustrations of cockpits: by Lars Jansson and Stig Borstell of Saab AB in providing illustrations and answering many questions about the design of cockpits from the A-21 to the JAS-39.

R.C. Snell of DERA helped in finding photographs of early cockpit equipment. Access to archive material and to modern cockpit technology was provided by Smiths Industries directors Russel Plumley and Nigel H. Hughes. Dr David Baker was most helpful in providing a link with American companies. Photographs were kindly provided by David Baker, Peter J. Cooper, Philip Jarrett, Peter Ottery and R. Wallace Clarke along with BAe Marketing Dept Warton, Joanne Nuwar of GQ Parachutes, Heather Cox of GEC-Marconi, Martin-Baker Ltd, McDonnell Douglas, Tom Cathcart of Museum of Flight at Everett WA, and Digital Image Design.

First published in the UK in 1999
by Airlife Publishing Ltd

British Library Cataloguing-in-Publication Data
A catalogue record for this book
is available from the British Library

ISBN 1 85310 915 0

Typeset by Servis Filmsetting Ltd, Manchester
Printed in England by Butler & Tanner Ltd,
Frome and London

Airlife Publishing Ltd
101 Longden Road, Shrewsbury, SY3 9EB, England

Contents

Dedicated to all who have had to grope and fumble, graze their knuckles and suffer frozen extremities and numbed *gluteus maximus*.

Introduction

Prologue

The lean man walked forward to the machine. With a reassuring glance at his companions standing to one side, he lay down on the assembly of wood and fabric and settled his weight in a cradle which half embraced his hips. His left hand grasped a short vertical lever, his right-hand adjusted the controls of a small petrol engine which lay alongside him.

The year was 1903 and for the first time mankind was to achieve controllable, powered flight in a machine which was heavier than the air in which it flew. 1903 marks a key point in the upward curve with which we describe the growth of technology. From the day the Wright brothers at Kill Devil Hills, North Carolina, made history the growth curve began to rise even more steeply.

The Wright brothers may have foreseen future developments in terms of performance but not a future in which flying machines would come to dominate politics and wars. And not the controls, instruments and aids to human vision and performance undreamed of in 1903.

Origins of cockpit

Within less than ten years of the Wright brothers' first successful heavier-than-air, powered, dirigible, flying machine, aircraft were being used for war. By 1914 the essential features had materialised from numerous experimental ideas and flights. A fuselage, wings and empennage, an engine and the vital human element and its position from which to exercise. control

Since those pioneering years a number of different names have been given to the place in an aircraft occupied by a pilot or by other crew members such as pilot's place, crew station, and cockpit. In civil transport aircraft and their military equivalent, 'flight deck' is frequently used. The origin of 'cockpit' as part of aviation terminology is uncertain. It so happened that many of the pre 1914 flying machines provided no protection to the pilot from the elements. Eventually the sides of the fuselage were raised and those designers and pilots who were also keen on sailing applied the nautical term 'cockpit' to their aircraft's control position. In the sailing world 'cockpit' is specified as a depression in the deck for the tiller and helmsman. Another meaning comes from the bloody sport of cock fighting. In the Royal Air Force Communiqués of 1918 we find 'cock-pit'.

Aviation etymological research can lead to many origins. Bill Gunston's definition in *Jane's Aerospace Dictionary* is: 'Space occupied by pilot or other occupants, especially if open at the top. Preferably restricted to small aircraft in which the occupants cannot move from their seats'.

The control position of the Wright Flyer of 1903 was not a cockpit within the accepted meaning of the word. As speed, altitude, manoeuvrability and anti-aircraft systems advanced decade by decade aircrew required greater and greater protection from the aerial environment and its hazards. As will be described, the progress from the Flyer to the 21st century may end with the elimination of human crew in combat aircraft.

The modern fighter/attack cockpit still exhibits features that have their origins in the first decade of powered, heavier-than-air flight. The pilot sits behind an instrument panel and faces forward. His feet operate the yaw control (rudder) and his hand controls roll and pitch (ailerons and elevator). In military transport aircraft the controls are similar to those of a civil aircraft.

Major elements

To state the obvious: the aircraft cockpit has five major elements. These are: the human pilot or crew member, the controls, the instruments, the location of the cockpit and the structure. The last item includes the fenestration. Therefore, when describing or commenting on a particular cockpit we need to consider each of the elements and their relationships that have or did exist between each other.

In 1903 the Wright brothers had no design manuals to which they could refer when deciding on the type and position of the controls. Good practical engineering sense placed the pilot and engine close to the centre of gravity of the Flyer. To meet this important requirement the pilot was given a prone position alongside the engine; the pilot to the left of the engine. The prone position owed much to the series of gliders the Wrights had perfected before they started on powered flight. And, in that respect, they followed the prone position pioneered by others such as Lilienthal and, much earlier, as proposed by Leonardo da Vinci. The prone pilot's position in the Wright Flyer also suited the hip-control used for wing warping (roll) and at the same time, as in the gliders, reduced the frontal area of the pilot and therefore the drag.

Despite the success of the Wright machines during the first ten years, they and other designers eventually abandoned the prone position in favour of the seated; although Santos Dumont stood at the controls of his 1906 machine. However, the prone position lurked in the designer's cupboard for the next 50 years. From time-to-time it was taken out and tried; either to fit in a confined fuselage or to alleviate G induced effects on the pilot of an agile aircraft. Designers have also assayed the supine positions for the pilot: of which more later.

In the first decade of powered flight each innovator usually had his own ideas about the way in which the controls should be operated and in which direction they should be moved to effect a particular control surface action. An important control arrangement, because it is the first, is that of the Wright Flyer of 1903. However, the controls of the Flyer did not necessarily become the ancestor of today's arrangement. Although pitch was controlled by the foreplane operating lever moving in the expected direction and can claim to be the progenitor of the joystick, roll and rudder control was effected by movement of the pilot's hips. In a later version of the Wright Flyer rudder or yaw control was also by a lever but this moved in a fore and aft plane and therefore was not the origin of the modern rudder bar or pedals. With the first Wright series, in which the pilot lay prone, his feet took no part in the control action. Although by 1908 the brothers had adopted a seated position for the pilot, it was not until 1912 that they equipped their machines with a rudder-bar.

Blériot's control

The 'father' of what eventually became the international hand and foot stereotype control is Blériot. His Type XI monoplane had a 'modern' joystick and rudder bar. The joystick of Blériot's *Cloche* control for wing warping and elevator combined the two functions and was moved in the directions we have come to expect. Irrespective of what did or did not happen in the first decade of aviation, by the onset of WWI the joystick movement, as we now know it, and the 'foot forward on the side to which we want to turn' stereotypes were well established. The origin of this 'opposite to a bicycle handlebars' arrangement is not known with any certainty. Some early flying machines did have the rudder bar moving in the same sense as that used by cyclists. One explanation is that it was simpler to arrange the cables from the ends of the rudder bar back to the rudder so that they were not crossed. This arrangement was the same as the tiller ropes of a boat.

Hand preference

Another factor that exercised the pioneer aviators related to a pilot's hand preference. By the end of the decade it was generally realised that a pilot's preferred hand, i.e. the right-hand in the majority, should be used on the control needing the greater sensitivity of touch and co-ordination.

Left-hand circuit

Related to these early control ideas are the subsequent left-hand circuit rule, the right-hand on stick and left on throttle in single-engine aircraft and the principal-pilot-to-the-left practices which became standard. German multi-engine bombers of WWI (World War One), such as the Gotha V, had the single pilot's position to the left of the centre line of the fuselage. However, this configuration was not adopted by British aircraft designers until ten years after WWI. The naval tradition of the starboard side being superior to the port may have influenced the decision to place the pilot of the RNAS/RAF heavy bombers in WWI to the right of the centre line. There is also the possible influence of the horse and horseless (early automobile) carriage driver's positions on the right.

A number of reasons have been given for the emergence of the left-hand circuit as the preferred direction when approaching an airfield and landing. One is the general custom or habit derived from the Olympic left-hand circling as used at competitive circling events such as horse racing and athletics. (However in the UK about half the National Hunt and flat racing courses were and are right-handed.) It is possible that another reason was the preference for avoiding a right-hand turn in the Camel. As the Camel was one of the principal types operated by the British air services its pilots may have exerted a strong influence on what eventually became a standard. There is also the preference pilots had of looking and leaning to the left rather than to the right and therefore across the arm and hand which were on the control column.

After WWI a start was made on international 'rules of the road' for civil aviation; but not necessarily of concern to military aviation. These were based on the rules adopted in the 19th century for shipping. In 1919 a 'keep right' on airways was adopted at an international convention on air navigation.

Human adaptability

Once aviation became, through the demands of war, the experience of thousands the question of a pilot's hand preference began to interest academics. However, human adaptability is such that not many pilots who were left-handed, for example, had any particular problem. Since those early years, all pilots have become accustomed to both left-hand on throttle and right-hand on throttle controls. However, in the majority of the world's single-seat and tandem-seat aircraft the right-hand on stick and left on throttle has been the usual arrangement for over 80 years.

Advanced ideas

In August 1914 heavier-than-air aviation had existed for barely eleven years. Although the advances made in aircraft design since the Wright brothers' flight may have seemed at the time to have been outstanding they were eclipsed during the following four years by a great leap in technology.

In WWI, there were many advanced ideas proposed for aircraft design and equipment but the pressure to keep always to maximum aircraft production rates meant that many had to be put on one side. To mention just two: turbo-supercharging and variable-pitch propellers; both of which would have added to the number of controls and instruments in the cockpit. Had the air war gone on into 1919 then all fighter aircraft and not just a few, would have been equipped with oxygen and a radio-telephone and an electrically-heated suit provided for the pilot. Similar equipment would have become standard for other aircraft, particularly for the heavy night bombers. By 1919 it is likely that the parachute would have been accepted as an essential item of equipment in the RAF: the German air services had already accepted it as an essential item and Irvin in the USA was about to prove the effectiveness of his seat-type parachute.

Cockpit design and consideration for the pilot's comfort and effectiveness as a specific discipline was low on a designer's list of tasks. Designers had many far more demanding problems to solve. For one, they were always having to make do with engines of lower power and reliability than they had expected. Hindsight is a cheap and readily available basis on which to criticise the mistakes of the past. Therefore although there are many critical comments on cockpit design and equipment in this book the author must emphasise that designers in the past were handicapped by one or all of the following circumstances:

1. No precedents.
2. None or few guides to good ergonomics.
3. The pressure of wartime production demands.
4. The frequent need to find room and places for more equipment.

Number of controls and instruments

Although the performance of aircraft in general has improved decade by decade since WWI the fundamental layout of the pilot's cockpit has remained close at all times to one stereotype. Of course there have been significant changes to the details; both in function and appearance. Between 1930 and about 1950 the important changes to the pilot's place in fighting aircraft related mainly to the number of controls and instruments. It has always been a basic factor that improvements in aircraft performance have usually predicated a greater number of instruments and controls.

In this book there are examples of specific cockpits and their equipment. But sometimes there have been many modifications during the life of an aircraft type. Therefore the reader's experience or knowledge of a particular type of aircraft may differ from the example given.

Crew positions

The title of this book does not include the word 'pilot' because it is intended to refer to all crew positions and not just to the pilot's place. There were and are crew positions for observers, artillery spotters, photographers, navigators, flying mechanics, flight engineers, and wire-less/radar/EW operators, nurses and loadmasters.

The positions provided for non-pilot crew members, such as navigators and gunners, have not changed as significantly as that of the pilot's place. Nevertheless the navigator's position in the mid-WWII era acquired more equipment, particularly in the shape of electronic aids to navigation. Even though by the mid-1930s it was realised that the increasing speed and operating altitudes of aircraft encouraged the development and installation of fully enclosed, power-operated, gun turrets the open gunner's cockpit of WWI lingered on into WWII.

Naval cockpits

The cockpits of aircraft designed for operating from the decks of aircraft carriers have differed only in small details from those of land planes. This is not surprising when we remember that the number of specialised 'carrier' aircraft types in the history of naval warfare is small compared with the hundreds of different types of military aircraft introduced over the past 90 years.

The helicopter and airship control positions

This book only describes the airship and helicopter control positions in passing. They are subjects deserving of books to themselves by authors with first-hand experience; particularly of the two-handed coordination needed to effect collective and cyclic control in a rotary-wing machine.

Unusual cockpits

Since the birth of heavier-than-air flying machines, for good or for other reasons, designers have schemed unusual and sometimes innovative shapes and locations for cockpits of pilots and other crew members. If some cockpits are described as extraordinary, then, for comparison, we must define what is meant by 'ordinary'. The 'ordinary' cockpit is likely to have all or at least some of the following characteristics:

> Its centre line coincident with the centre line of the fuselage.
> Seated positions for the pilots.
> Located close to the 'sharp' end of the fuselage.

In general the pilots of single-engine aircraft have been seated on the fuselage centre line and above the level of the monoplane or the lower wing of a biplane. Of course there have been numerous examples which do not meet all or one of the above requirements; some have been accepted as normal because of special circumstances or because the aircraft was virtually a single-engine type which happened to have two or more engines. Above all, the subject is hedged about by exceptions and examples which disprove any rules.

Modern cockpit design

In about 1950 the cockpit design teams began to shrug off some of the traditions of the previous 36 years and to embrace technologies that would have been strange to the airmen of earlier years. At the same time pilots and others became increasingly aware that the aircraft was imposing hazardous environmental conditions in the cockpit. At this point in aviation history the psychologists and ergonomic specialists began to play an important role in the design of the cockpit.

The future

We cannot be certain about the future. The pace of change in technology usually increases more quickly than expected. What can be predicted, however, with a degree of certainty, based on present day trends, is the greater use of aircraft having no human crew and therefore the cockpit, as we now know it, may be consigned to history. We have already seen the effective use of the VI unmanned aircraft of WWII. In more recent times there have been the Tomahawk missiles which devastated key installations in Iraq. There are also a number of unmanned surveillance aircraft now in use and they are set to perform an ever increasing role for both strategic and tactical sorties. These suggest that in the first decade of the 21st century there will be many more uninhabited aerial vehicles (UAVs).

Each chapter has been related roughly in span of years to emphasise the effects the two world wars have had on advancing cockpit technology. The role of the historical references is to establish the origins of today's stereotypes and their applicability to the future and to highlight lessons to be learnt from the mistakes of the past and present.

Mankind and machine

In the chapters which follow much is written about aircraft and the controls and instruments in their cockpits. Also mentioned are the effects to which the human is subjected when flying of noise, vibration, stress, physical loads imposed by G and extremes of light and temperature.

Before considering specific cockpits and aircraft the reader may find some observations on the human element useful as background information. Mankind, which by definition includes all sexes, has evolved over millions of years. Yet at the same time human physical abilities have hardly changed at all, even though mental potential and ability advanced significantly once our branch of the anthropoids evolved verbal communication. Whereas machines have evolved over a comparatively much shorter time span and only in the last few decades have started to acquire intelligence.

Movement over the earth's surface and swinging about in the trees imposed no particular stress on the human frame and constitution. Using logs, canoes and later vessels to navigate rivers and the seas made no particular demands on the body; except of course, on those who ventured on the high seas and experienced a form of motion sickness induced by the undulating sea.

An old saying is; 'If man had been intended to move about by any means other than under his or her own locomotion the human structure and organs would have evolved to a different arrangement'. This refers to the fact that most types of vehicle impose an environment which is not necessarily in accord with our physical and psychological natures. Irrespective of the length of a journey or the speed attained our sensory organs remain those of an animal whose basic and original specification included a speed restriction of around 350 feet per minute walking and 1,500 feet per minute when sprinting. Until the advent of the flying machine, mankind, in general, spent most of the time moving in a two-dimensional world. Once mankind exceeded the limitations of motion, which had applied during the evolution of the anthropoids into *homo sapiens*, adverse effects, such as motion sickness and disorientation, imposed a new set of limitations on the extent to which mankind could move away from the original set of physical limitations.

The flying machine has come on the scene in the last second of the vast time span of human evolution. Man has not had time in which to evolve in ways which will combat the effects of motion sickness, disorientation, exposure to unusual positions in three-dimensional space, confinement in one position for hours and being translated rapidly from one time zone to another.

Today's men and women are little different physically from those of the Neolithic period but are expected to live and work in a very different and often far more demanding environment.

The rapid advance of technology

In 1920 a small book could have been written which would have contained all that was known at the time about the design of the cockpit and its equipment. Today, its equivalent would be many inches thick and be out of date before it went to press.

CHAPTER ONE

1914 – 1918

Start of air power

Experience of air power, albeit in a limited way, was first gained by the Italian air force in 1911 in Libya, by the United States Army on the Mexican border in 1913 and by the United States Navy at Vera Cruz early in 1914. However, August 1914 is the convenient year to start this survey of the aircraft cockpit and its development because the next four years saw an unexpected and massive increase in the number of aircraft, in the number of different types and the cumulative experiences of thousands of pilots and other flyers.

Aircraft types of 1914

The Royal Flying Corps (RFC) that moved to France in August 1914 had two basic types of aircraft: the tractor, engine-in-front, biplane and the pusher biplane. The tractor types were represented by the BE. The pushers included the FEs (Farman Experimental). There were few monoplanes because earlier the RFC had decided they were structurally unsound. However the German

The Handley Page 'Yellow Peril' of 1913. Although not intended as a military aircraft, nevertheless the cockpit equipment is representative of the limited technology available for all types of aircraft in the years prior to WWI.
(Smiths Industries)

air service was less concerned about any real or apparent structural shortcomings of the monoplane. The Fokker Eindecker (i.e. one plane) performed well and for a time in 1915 became the scourge of the RFC. The French air force used both pusher and tractor aircraft. Not until the last year of WWI did the US air services join in the air war to a significant degree; and then primarily using European-designed aircraft. It would be some years later that American innovation and ideas for the cockpit began to emerge.

The BE 2, used by the RFC at the beginning of WWI, had two very open cockpits. The sides came up only as far as the occupants' elbows. In the improved BE, the 2c, the cockpit sides were higher; thereby reducing the drag caused by the crew's bodies. The BE 2c introduced the question: which of the two seats should be for the pilot? In the BE 2c the pilot sat aft even though when it became necessary to carry defensive armament the observer in the front seat was hemmed in by struts and wires. It was some time before aircraft design in general positioned the pilot in front of the observer in tractor-propeller machines.

The DH 1 followed the BE 2c to France. This had the 'Farman' pusher arrangement of engine and crew. The pilot sat behind the observer who occupied the front of what was nothing more than the engine nacelle extended forward. The crew out in front was less affected by the noise of the engine and had an exceptional view on all sides. The FE 2b was similar. The 'pushers' were to a large extent the result of a lack of an effective method of firing a machine gun through the disc of a propeller without hitting a blade.

The FE 8 of 1915 had, for its time, a carefully streamlined nacelle to accommodate gun, pilot, fuel-tank and engine; in that order. It was suggested at the time that the aluminium cladding of the nacelle provided the pilot with some protection against enemy fire. The thin aluminium scantlings were not riveted to the structure of the airframe but laced on; as with conventional fabric covering. The single Lewis gun in the FE 8 was initially mounted low down in the nose of the nacelle and just ahead of the control column and above the pilot's shins. The gun was allowed a limited degree of traverse. In line with the pilot's eye point was a sighting bar. The sighting bar and

combined hand-grip was linked to the gun and had a downward projecting portion whereby the pilot could move the gun. This arrangement may have been decided upon in order to simplify changing ammunition drums; an important requirement in 1915 because at that time a drum only held 47 rounds (a three-second burst of fire).

Fixed gun

The conclusions of those on the staff, who may not have had any practical air fighting experience, were in conflict with the FE 8 pilots at the 'sharp end'. The pilots wanted to use the gun with the fixing clamp in place so that they only had to aim the aircraft and not try and fly and move the gun at the same time. Staff officers did not always appreciate the complication of having to fly with one hand so as to leave the other free to operate the gun and not having a third hand to operate the engine controls. However, to be fair to the staff, few, if any, in the RFC and RNAS appreciated the advantages of the fixed gun, whereas both the French and the Germans lost little time in adopting the fixed forward-firing gun and perfecting methods for firing through the disc of a tractor propeller .

A contemporary report on the FE 8 cockpit and its equipment remarks that the hand pump for pressurising the fuel tank and associated change-over cock were awkwardly positioned. The pilot's seat was reported as 'comfortable'. However the author of the report did not like the resulting backward inclination of the pilot's body. A more upright position was recommended. Another suggestion was that the gun be raised. An important comment related to visibility and the effectiveness of the windscreen and the fact that pilots did not necessarily have to wear goggles. Nevertheless the gun mounting and its position engendered much adverse comment once the FE 8 entered squadron service.

In 1917 RFC ace Albert Ball was involved with the design of the Austin Fighting Biplane (AFB 1). The designer interpreted Ball's ideas as best he could. He located the pilot's eye point level with the upper wing so as to give maximum forward view. To give some downward view there were large cut-outs in the lower wing on each side. The arcs of view from the cockpit were compared with those from the cockpit of the Sopwith Camel. As the pilot's view from the cockpit of the Camel was one of the more restrictive the designer of the AFB 1 had little difficulty in doing better and being able to report that: 'The general opinion is that the view from the Austin Fighter is considerably superior to that from the Camel.' Interestingly this is one of the earliest examples of using pinhole camera photographs from the pilot's eye point to establish the arcs of view.

Ball wanted the AFB 1 to have a Vickers gun mounted at the pilot's knees, just forward of the control column, and firing through the hollow propeller shaft of the geared engine. However there was not enough room so a Lewis had to be specified. This is where the problem of changing ammunition drums when flying above 15,000 feet had to be considered. Above that altitude the lack of oxygen made any physical effort, other than flying the aircraft, extremely difficult if not impossible. The pilot also had to change the drum of the upper Lewis gun on its Foster mounting. However these problems did not have to be faced because the AFB 1 did not go into production because it was no improvement on the SE 5 which was already in full scale production.

In English language histories of air warfare there are a number of items of equipment named after their inventors. For example: Foster, Hutton, Neame, Maxim, Sutton and others. An important example is Scarff whose rotatable and elevatable mounting for a machine-gun provided a flexible and easy-to-handle method of aiming. It became a recognisable feature of the air gunner's cockpit in British aircraft for the next twenty years.

Weights

Throughout WWI designers had to make careful judgements over how much weight could be allocated to a particular item such as guns, bombs, fuel and crew. For example the Sopwith Tabloid weighed less than 1200 lb all-up. The structure took up 30%, the engine 38% and the fuel 15%. The remaining 17% had to allow for pilot and armament. Therefore the cockpit and its equipment had to be simple and light. Because the pilot had to wear many layers of clothing,

including a heavy leather flying coat, to keep out the cold, this was a further debit item in the weight and balance sheet.

The camera's eye

It was not long into WWI before armies realised that photographs taken from the air provided valuable 'over the hill' information about the enemy's dispositions and intentions. The camera provided a more reliable and accurate record than that brought back by mounted scouts. The first cameras were hand-held (both hands), heavy and bulky. They required ten or more setting operations for each exposure.

When leaning over the side of the cockpit into the freezing slipstream the observer found it very difficult to keep the camera truly vertical. The next development was to fix the camera to the aircraft so as to simplify the operator's task. Some Renault-powered BE 2cs were fitted with a conical box-camera mounted vertically to starboard outside the pilot's cockpit. The choice of the starboard side for the camera is interesting in the light of subsequent side and hand preference considerations. The location allowed the pilot to use his right hand when changing the glass plates. A similar mounting on the starboard side was used for the bomb sight when BE 2cs were equipped with release racks for two 112-lb bombs.

Improvement in camera technology followed as the general staffs of all three armies on the Western Front demanded more and better aerial photographs. One example is the semi-automatic plate changing mechanism. This was operated remotely by the pilot through a Bowden cable shutter release. Another lead released each exposed plate so that it fell into a box. If an observer was carried then another box of plates could be exchanged for the used one. The aircraft had to be level fore and aft and the wings level when the shutter was triggered. Altogether photographic flights required precise navigation and aircraft control in order to produce a series of photo prints which could be joined to form a mosaic of the battlefield. Observers used hand-held cameras for oblique shots.

Bomb sights

It was not until the middle of 1915 that a proper, scientifically-designed, bomb sight, as opposed to two nails in a piece of wood, was developed for the RFC. This was the CFS (Central Flying School) type used with a stop watch to time the apparent movement of the target between the fixed sight and the moveable foresight. It remained in use up to the end of 1916.[1]

One pilot's comments emphasise the difficulties of using the new bomb sight:

'No sooner had I tried the bomb sight in the air than I realised that it would be utterly impossible for me to learn to use it in under two days' time. A rather complicated apparatus, it required some skill and experience in the using. Above all it required two flights over the target: the first one to get the wind's speed and direction and to make sundry calculations with a stopwatch and notebook, the second flight to drop the bombs. Since observers had to be dispensed with owing to the added weight of bombs, all the calculations had to be done by the pilot. I did not fancy myself sitting above an angry Archie (Flak) battery and scratching my head over a complicated sum in arithmetic, especially if the result was to be the totally inaccurate placing of my bombs. The more I thought of it the less the prospect pleased me.'[2]

In 1916 the Royal Aircraft Factory at Farnborough UK (later the RAE/DERA) developed a periscopic bomb sight. This was tested in a Martinsyde Elephant. As with the previously described method of aiming bombs, the RAF sight required all the pilot's attention. After setting height and ground speed on the sight and checking that he was flying directly into or down wind, the pilot had to keep his left eye on the fore-and-aft bubble inclinometer, to ensure level flight, and at the same time, with his right eye on the eye-piece of the sight, keep the target against the cross-wires. Altogether a lot of things to be done and fly the aircraft, particularly if the enemy was contesting the operation.[3] As the war progressed and bomb sights improved, training towers were built at some schools. These enabled a pupil to operate a bomb sight while looking down at a representation of the ground painted on a moving belt. This was another precursor of the modern simulator.

In August 1914 the RNAS was not only quick in establishing air stations along the Channel coast between Calais and Dunkirk and taking the war to the enemy, it also played an important part in the Dardenelles campaign of early 1915. Wing Commander Samson, RNAS Dardenelles, ordered that his pilots always had to be armed with a revolver or pistol, carry binoculars, a life-saving waistcoat or an empty petrol can. The observers had to carry a rifle, life-saving equipment, binoculars and the proper charts.[4]

Unusual places

Providing unusual locations for the pilot's cockpit was a characteristic of many designers during WWI. The Booth design of an anti-airship fighter armed with a Davis recoilless QF gun positioned the pilot's place on top of the centre section.

The absence of a reliable interrupter gear encouraged the development of the SPAD A2 for the French air service. The observer/gunner sat in a nacelle mounted ahead of the tractor propeller. On the ground the nacelle could be hinged downward to give access to the engine. Did the occupant ever worry that the securing bolts might work loose in flight? A similar gunner's cockpit was arranged for the BE 9 of the RFC. This was mounted on a ball race bearing on the front of the propeller shaft and stayed by a system of struts extending forward and upward from the undercarriage. The occupant of this box out in front certainly had an excellent view but must have been very aware of the four-bladed propeller thrashing through the air immediately behind his head. Every landing must have been a 'white knuckle' affair.

The squadron selected to try the BE 9 quickly returned it to the depot. Nevertheless the Royal Aircraft Factory at Farnborough persisted with the cockpit ahead of the propeller idea and designed the FE 10. This was to be a single-engine fighter with the engine between the wings and the propeller revolving just clear of the leading edges of the wings. The pilot and a Lewis gun would have been in a cockpit carried on struts out in front, as in the BE 9. Eventually the successful development of the gun-interrupter gear did away with the need for unusual relationships and the FE 10 was re-drawn as a 'conventional' tractor fighter. The pilot's view ahead was obstructed by the centre section and by the lower wing. The designers of the twin-engine Bristol TTA paid even less attention to the arcs-of-view needed by the pilot. The cockpit was behind the wings and with a long nose ahead. The engine nacelles obscured most of the view to left and right. There was no provision for any system of communication between the pilot and the gunner other than gesticulations.

An enclosed pilot's place

From time to time during WWI designers experimented with transparent materials for enclosing the cockpit but they were either structurally weak or the pilots did not like the idea.

In December 1915 the prototype of Handley Page's O/100 twin-engine bomber flew from Hendon airfield in north-west London. For its time it exhibited an early example of a completely enclosed pilot's cabin. The pilot sat on the centre-line behind a vertical wedge-shaped windscreen. Unfortunately the window structure was not strong enough and during one flight it collapsed. RNAS pilots disliked it because of misting and reflections. Harald Penrose commented that: '. . . though what they really felt was claustrophobia because they were conditioned to open cockpits'.[5] An attitude that would persist for another 15 years. Therefore, subsequent versions and its descendants the O/400 and V/1500, had an open pilots' cockpit. Although the plural possessive for pilots is used it should be noted that in the majority of British multi-engine aircraft only one set of controls was provided.

The O/100 was eagerly awaited by the RNAS crews. However they had to wait until serious tail vibration had been eliminated. Even after redesigning the structure the tail still vibrated once the speed reached 75 knots. The Handling Notes for the HP O/100 referred to the unusual position of the pilot, about 12 ft ahead of the CG, that had a tendency to exaggerate all movements of the aircraft. This was in contrast to the majority of aircraft of the time in which the pilot sat close to the CG. The larger aircraft became the larger their control surfaces and, in spite of aerodynamic or mass balancing, the heavier became the loads on the pilot's hands and feet.

Another early example of an enclosed pilot's position is, for its time, the 'giant' A D 1000 twin-fuselage, three-engine seaplane bomber for the RNAS. It had a bullet-proof 'greenhouse' in the nose. An assessment of its flying qualities included the comment: 'It took 15 miles to unstick and get airborne, but could not attain more than 70 knots, which was not far above the stall . . . [there would have been an] immense reduction of resistance and weight if the bullet-proof glass greenhouse were replaced with an open Maurice Farman type nacelle.'[6] The reference to speed is a reminder that modern aviation also uses knots as a standard for speed. In WWI the RFC used mph and only the RNAS/ RAF maritime patrol aircraft crews used knots. French and German aircraft had airspeed indicators calibrated in km/hr.

The Short 166 torpedo-bomber of 1915, a single-engine floatplane, provides another example of the pilot's forward view being of secondary consideration. The heat exchanger (radiator) for the engine cooling system was mounted on top of the fuselage above the engine and directly in the pilot's forward line of sight. Perhaps the long established practice, handed down from the days of sail, of not necessarily providing the officer conning a ship with an unwooded view applied also to aircraft.

Pemberton Billing's Night Hawk, the drawings of which bear R. J. Mitchell's signature, was a twin-engine quadriplane. A crew position with Scarff ring for a Lewis gun was mounted level with the uppermost wing to give a 360-degree field of fire. A similar cockpit, but forward of the leading edge of the upper wing, was used in the Vickers FB 11. The Sopwith LRTTr (Long Range Tractor Triplane) escort fighter had a streamlined gunner's nacelle merged with the centre section. However it did not go into service but it did lead to the Sopwith Triplane fighter.

The Armstrong Whitworth FK 12 triplane, designed by Koolhoven, solved the problem of forward fire outside the propeller disc in a single-engine tractor aircraft by providing a gunner's nacelle at each side mounted on the middle wing. Apart from any technical shortcomings the FK 12 was not put into production. Interestingly the term 'escort fighter' was sometimes applied to

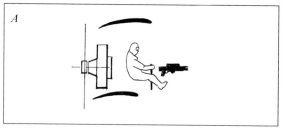

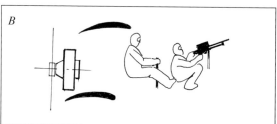

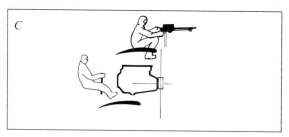

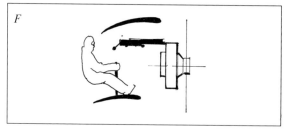

these strange aircraft. This reflected the airwar tactics of early 1916. Over the Western Front the RFC was facing increasing opposition from German fighters to its routine photographic and artillery ranging sorties. They needed protection.

Variations of the principal elements

As the war progressed and the design offices sought to meet the demands of the air war, there were many variations of the principal elements that together made a particular aircraft type. These variations included: gun-pilot-propeller-engine; propeller-gun-pilot; gun-pilot-engine-propeller; gunner-pilot-engine-propeller; propeller-engine-gun-pilot and propeller-engine-gun-pilot-gunner-gun. The method of classifying aircraft cockpits in relation to the other principal elements can be extended to include the fuel tank. In many aircraft types the fuel tank was positioned adjacent to the engine. In the event of a crash or even a carburettor fire in the air, the crew was unlikely to survive the ensuing inferno. Not until the end of WWI did design offices consider providing a fire-retarding bulkhead between engine and fuel tank. The 'Farman' pusher arrangement gave the pilot in front a good view ahead but at the risk of being crushed by the engine in the event of a crash.

As we have seen, some of the different combinations and arrangements of propeller, guns, engine, tanks and crew were nothing more than experiments. Nevertheless they indicate that the fighter, in particular, might have finished up in 1918 as pusher or shaft-driven tractor type had these proved to be successful. For example, the Beardmore WB IV experimental naval aircraft, with its amidships engine and pilot in front just

Single-engine aircraft variations in relative positions of pilot, observer/gunner, guns and engine. 1914–c. 1935.

A. e.g. DH 1, DH 2 and FE 8
B. e.g. FE 2a/b and FB 5
C. e.g. FB 11 and Sopwith LRTT
D. e.g. BE 9 and SPAD A2
E. e.g. Bristol Fighter and the majority of two-seat fighter, observation and bomber aircraft between 1916 and 1935.
F. e.g. Camel and majority of single-seat fighters from WWI onward.
(Author)

behind the shaft-driven propeller, might have set the standard for years to come. Until the end of the propeller-driven fighter era designers assayed one or more of the unusual arrangements listed previously. In the 30s and 40s there were tandem twin-engine, one pulling and one pushing, fighters. However the 'conventional' engine in front of the pilot arrangement tended to dominate fighter design from 1918 onward. The Sopwith 1½ Strutter went into production with the gunner aft of the pilot. From then on that became the accepted arrangement for the majority of two-seat tractor types.

Throughout 1916 there were a number of twin-engine aircraft assayed for the RFC and the RNAS. At that time classifications such as fighter, artillery spotting, photography and bombing were rarely applied rigorously to a particular design because the air services, particularly the RFC, were called upon to perform all four roles with whatever aircraft were available. The FE 4, for example, was designed initially as a ground-attack machine although when it first flew the armament was not defined. It is of interest in the history of the cockpit because of the unusual shape of the forward part of the fuselage. It resembled a shoe with the heel leading in the direction of flight. There was a small transparent section in the 'back' of the shoe and two large nosewheels of the undercarriage at the front.

The fixed forward-facing Lewis gun in front of

Vickers Gunbus c. 1915 in an unusual setting. Compared with many tractor propeller aircraft the crew had an uninterrupted view.
(Vickers)

the pilot of the DH 2 proved a popular arrangement for combating German fighters and ensuring that the RFC always took the war to the enemy. The DH 2 is one of the first types to present the pilot with the problem and the dangers of the gyroscopic couple effect from the spinning rotary engine. For example when making a right-hand turn the pilot had to use left rudder. Should he instinctively use right rudder then he could be in serious trouble; at the least he would lose speed; at the worst a spin would result. The DH 2 earned the appellation 'spinning incinerator' following numerous spins. Experienced pilots only became 'experienced' once they learnt to centralise the rudder quickly at the onset of a skidding turn. An RFC pilot's comment on the gyroscopic effect was : 'There was the same quick lurch of the wings as engine came on and off . . .'[7]

Rotary engines

Control of the rotary engines of this violent period in aviation development had to be exercised with great care. Usually there were four items: ignition switch or switches, fuel fine adjustment, throttle and 'blip' switch. The 'blip' switch allowed the pilot to cut the engine momentarily without having to use the throttle and 'fine' control levers. It was not wise to try and control the engine with the throttle alone because for each position there was an optimum fine adjustment lever setting. Failure to achieve the correct combination could result in the engine stopping. This may not have been of consequence well above the ground but when taking off and landing could be fatal to the pilot. We have to remember that these early flying machines, with only modest engine power over a limited range of rpm, had considerable drag from the wires, struts and the many excrescences. The moment the engine stopped the aircraft immediately lost flying speed. If there was insufficient height in which to put the nose down and gain speed, the aircraft would spin in. Therefore during the approach to a landing the pilot used the 'blip' switch on the control column to control thrust and to avoid stopping the engine completely.

The Gnome Monosoupape 150 hp rotary engine in some Sopwith Camels had an adjustable ignition system. This allowed the pilot to operate the engine on one, three, five, seven or nine cylinders as a means of controlling thrust.

Sopwith Pup

Although not the only RFC/RNAS fighter in which the designer concentrated the principal weights close to the CG, the Sopwith Pup of 1916, in side elevation, emphasised the close proximity of engine, pilot, gun and fuel tank. One of the disadvantages of positioning the pilot close to the aircraft's CG and therefore close to the centre of lift, was the lack of view forward and up. The pilot's head was close to the trailing edge of the upper wing. In the Pup and in many other types, the centre section trailing edge was cut back. Sopwith also used transparent Cellon in place of fabric on the centre section. A feature of the Pup's cockpit was a knob sliding in a horizontal slot to the right of the pilot which operated the adjustable tailplane. The Bristol monoplane scout that flew for the first time in June 1916 was not only a far more streamlined craft than its contemporaries; it also gave the pilot an all-round uninterrupted view.

Missing the prop.

Not until May 1915 did synchronising or interrupter systems come into use that enabled a gun or guns to fire through the propeller disc of tractor-type aircraft. Until then pilots had to make do with guns mounted at a considerable angle to the line of flight. Any schemes for mounting guns away from the cockpit in more favourable positions were unacceptable because of the need to attend to the frequent stoppages to which guns were prone at that time.

In 1913 an interrupter gear was patented by Schneider, the Swiss-born designer employed by LVG Werke in Germany. It was taken up and developed in England by the Edwards brothers. However it was turned down by the War Office as an unnecessary complication. In the same year Saulnier developed a gun/engine synchronising system. The idea was sound but the ammunition had an unpredictable delay between the firing pin striking a round and the bullet leaving the muzzle so that some rounds were striking the propeller.

SE5A. The arming (cocking) lever for the single Vickers 7.7mm gun is top left in the cockpit. There are two triggers on the control column: one for the Vickers gun and the other for a Lewis gun on a Foster mounting. An Aldis collimated sight is mounted in front of the windscreen.
(British Aerospace)

The system was abandoned in 1914. In its place came the Garros deflector plate arrangement that diverted any bullets whose path happened to coincide with a passing blade. The Germans captured a Morane-Saulnier parasol monoplane fitted with deflector plates on the propeller blades. On realising the reason for recent French successes, particularly by Lt Roland Garros, Fokker installed an interrupter gear, possibly based on the Schneider system, in a Fokker monoplane. From May 1915 onward German fighters were equipped with synchronised forward-firing guns. The British had access to a number of different interrupter gears. As well as the Schneider, these included the Scarff, Kauper and Constantinesco. The last avoided the use of difficult-to-maintain mechanical linkages. It was a hydraulic system developed by Constantinesco and Colley, hence CC gear. Here was another system that required additional equipment in the cockpit in the shape of hand pump for pressurising the hydraulic reservoir.

As noted, the advent of gun-interrupter or synchronising gears made many pusher and multi-engine designs unnecessary. This meant that unusual gun, engine and cockpit arrangements were abandoned either at the drawing board or at the prototype stages.

The second SE 5 that flew for the first time in December 1916 was one of the first RFC types to be equipped with an Aldis collimating gun sight in addition to the conventional ring and bead system. The tube of the Aldis became a familiar item of cockpit 'furniture'; albeit it was mounted on top of the engine nacelle and forward of the windscreen and did not necessarily project into the cockpit. It is sometimes incorrectly referred to as a 'telescopic' sight. In its usual form the Aldis sight did not magnify. It contained a system of lens that projected an aiming dot and circle focused at infinity. The pilot did not have to close one eye and keep his head in one precise position when using the sight.

An SE 5a was also used to test an armament of three Lewis guns mounted at 45 degrees on the centre section. By the time the trials were completed the Zeppelins had been replaced by Gotha bombers and this form of attack was no longer needed. To improve the kill probability when attacking airships or aircraft at night, fighters were equipped with the Neame sight. This had an electrically illuminated ring. The diameter of the ring was such that at 100 yards a Gotha bomber's wing span fitted the ring.[8]

The Albatros DI of the German air service arrived over the French battlefield in August 1916. It was a streamlined biplane fighter. The cockpit

A 7.7mm Lewis gun with 47-round magazine on a Foster mounting in a night fighter Avro 504K c. 1917. The ring against the windscreen was pulled to unlock the gun so that it could be pulled down to the vertical position when changing the magazine or to the 45 degree position when engaging an airship from below. The fore and back sights are illuminated as are the sights in front of the windscreen.

Neame illuminated sight seen in use during an attack on a Gotha night bomber.
(R. Wallace Clarke)

positioned the pilot with his eyes just below the centre section. The gap between the centre section and the fuselage was largely taken up by the twin Maxim machine-guns. This is the point to comment on two aspects of aviation history that have become confused over the years by writers and film makers. The guns of German fighters of WWI are often described as 'Spandau' whereas they were Maxim guns and little different in action from the Maxim/Vickers of British machines. Also film makers have persisted in making their actor pilots use the cocking (arming) levers as triggers when in fact they were triggered from the control column. In some films a special firing lever has been positioned between the gun breeches so that the audience would realise that the pilot was firing his guns.

Formation flying

On 14 January 1916 HQ RFC ordered that a reconnaissance aircraft had to be escorted by at least three other fighting machines (sic). Thus

BE 2c night fighter c. 1917 with twin Lewis gun armament. The guns are shown in the 'reload' position. The long lever outside the cockpit was used to position the guns at the inclined firing angle for attacking airships from below.
(British Aerospace)

formation flying, as it became known, became a part of aviation practice and history. The effect of formation flying on the design and equipment of the cockpit was indirect but nevertheless deserves mentioning. For example, it influenced the retention of the open cockpit because of the need for hand and arm signals by the leader of a formation. Until the advent of reliable and effective RT, 'zogging', as the arm signals came to be known in the RFC/RAF, had to suffice.[9]

One hand signal that did not appear until the latter half of WWI was 'Chocks away' for the simple reason that chocks were either not always available or considered necessary. The mechanic swinging the propeller relied on the resistance of the tail-skid and the inertia of the aircraft to avoid being cut down when the engine 'fired'.

Parachutes

Parachutes were supplied for the safety of observation balloon crews early on in WWI. These were hung on the side of the basket and were opened by a static line attached to the basket. The crews of German naval airships also used the attached type. However there is no record of airshipmen saving their lives by parachuting. An example of fearlessness is that of the airship commanders who preferred to keep down weight and therefore gain height by dispensing with parachutes for their crews. The Heinicke, an attached type parachute, was introduced into the German air service in 1918. This was worn with an integral harness and among those pilots who survived the destruction of their machine by enemy fire, by taking to their parachute, was Ernst Udet.

The 'parachute' debate occupied both pilots and air staff of the RFC/RNAS/RAF during the closing months of WWI. Among the arguments against adopting the Calthrop 'Guardian Angel' parachute, as provided for observers in balloons, was its weight. With its canister and static line it weighed 70 lb. As mentioned, in a Sopwith Tabloid, for example, only about 200 lb of the all-up weight of 1,200 lb was available for a pilot and armament. It was a question of a gun or a parachute. Another argument against parachutes came from those who directed the RFC and RNAS, but did not have to fly. Some were of the

German twin-engine bomber c. 1917. Three gun positions.
Pilot's position on left of cockpit. (Imrie)

opinion that a pilot with a parachute would be tempted to abandon his aircraft rather than face the enemy. Another type of parachute evaluated was the Mears. Tests of the stowage arrangement were carried out in an SE 5a.

Muscle power

At the end of 1916 Handley Page was planning to go into production with, for its time, giant O/100 twin-engine bomber. As mentioned, here was an aircraft whose control surfaces were larger than many pilots had met before and the length of the control wires from the cockpit introduced an entirely new 'feel'. In consequence the aileron

control wheel was large to give the pilot some purchase and to allow for the inevitable slack in the cables. There was only one throttle lever. This operated both engines together, but if the large knob on top was rotated engine power could be differentially applied. Turning the knob clockwise increased the thrust of the port engine and anti-clockwise of the starboard engine. This system was also used in the Vickers Vimy and later in the Virginia but positioned to the left of the pilot seated on the right.

Harald Penrose's comments on the handling of WWI aircraft are important. 'Few of the thousands of war pilots ever analytically studied control behaviour. Whether flying bomber, fighter, or seaplane, there seemed no more to it than that the machine either responded to their instinctive senses, making smooth sweet turns, or felt as though it had a will of its own and skidded and swung with ugly intent.'[10] At the same time few pilots seemed to have analysed the type and position of the controls and instruments in the cockpit. Detailed comments on the subject of what we now know as ergonomics are hard to find among the airwar literature of 1914–1918. With a very limited range of engine and aircraft speeds, few engine instruments and with the knowledge that if something were to go wrong there was little that could be done but hope, the pilot was often far more concerned with what was going on in the sky around him than what was happening or available in the cockpit.

Lloyd C11 c. 1917. Unusual in having the engine controls to the right in a single-seat cockpit. The Bosche starting magneto (right), with handle, is similar to those fitted to Allied aircraft in WWI. Bosche dominated the engine ignition market before the war and the Allies continued to manufacture copies after 1914. (Smiths Industries Archives)

Few of the German aces, when recounting their flying experiences commented on the instruments and controls. Perhaps, like most pilots of those years, they were far more concerned with staying alive than making erudite observations on the ergonomics of their cockpits.

Training

At the end of 1916 Smith-Barry was appointed commander of No 1 Reserve Squadron RFC Gosport with a free hand to use his training methods. He selected the Avro 504 as the basic training machine. He also insisted that the instructor occupied the front cockpit and not the safer, in the event of a crash, rear seat.

The front cockpit of the Avro 504K had the usual control column and rudder bar but no instruments other than a fuel contents indicator in the form of a sight glass. The other controls were: the handle of the tank pressurising pump,

the electrical master switch and the 'running' switch and the main fuel cock, 'blip' switch on control column and the two engine control levers. The pupil's cockpit in the 504K had an array of instruments similar to that of the first-line aircraft to which he hoped to graduate: compass, cross-level inclinometer, rpm, altimeter, airspeed, fuel tank air pressure, and oil pulsometer. The controls were a duplicate set of those in the front cockpit.

Not until 1917 was there a reasonable method of communication between instructor and pupil. Smith-Barry's Gosport speaking-tube solved the problem and obviated much of the need for arm and hand signals. It remained in use in RAF trainers until the end of WWII. Another method of 'communication' consisted of a wooden mallet which an instructor could use on any pupil who 'froze' on the controls.

Sopwith Camel

The Sopwith Camel in the hands of an experienced pilot held its own against the best that Germany could put in the air. In the hands of an inexperienced pilot and, of course, most pupil pilots were very inexperienced, it could be lethal. It would quickly flick into a spin in a right-hand turn if the speed was too low. Only in the last months of WWI was a two-seat version produced. This enabled a pupil to be taught how to avoid getting into trouble and how to get out of a spin.

Sopwith Camel. Dominating the cockpit are the two Vickers 7.7mm guns. Behind the cockpit can be seen the fuel tank cap. The triangular grip at the top of the control column has two triggers for the guns and a 'press-to-blip' switch. The white athwartships tube below the instrument panel is the air intake to the rotary engine.
(Philip Jarrett)

It also enabled an instructor to demonstrate the correct way to execute a right-hand turn.

Sopwith Dolphin

At the end of 1917 Sopwith produced the Dolphin as a successor to the Camel. The design took the principle of concentrating large items close to the CG and maximising the pilot's arcs of view to the extreme. The pilot sat with his feet against the back of the engine and his head partly protruding above the cabane. He was surrounded by the cabane structure and in front by the twin Vickers guns. There was also provision for two Lewis guns mounted at eye-level on the cross member of the structure. In the event of the aircraft crashing on its back the pilot had little chance of escaping. The pilot was 'close mewed up'.

Instruments of WWI

Before the war few aircraft had more than one or two instruments in the cockpit. During the war few aircraft had more than six. The essential set consisted of: airspeed indicator, altimeter, bubble lateral level, compass, fuel pressure gauge and pulsometer. The last item was a sight glass in which the pilot could see that the engine oil pump was working correctly by observing the pulses of oil. Some cockpits might have an ammeter.

The Bristol two-seat fighter F2 B of 1917 was designed 'to mix it' with enemy fighters in a dog fight as if it were an SE 5 or Camel. An interesting feature of the cockpit controls was the

Avro 504K of WWI with few instruments: inclinometer for flying wings level, pulsometer (bottom of panel) and pump for pressurising the fuel tank. (Smiths Industries Archives)

WWI altimeter used by RFC, RNAS and RAF. Note the pointer moves anticlockwise for increasing height.
(Smiths Industries)

Typical WWI British airspeed indicator. Few aircraft could touch 160, even in a dive.
(Smiths Industries)

adjustable treads on the rudder bar and the reserve control column on the right-side of the observer/gunner's cockpit. The F2 B had, for its

time, an impressive array of instruments and controls in the front cockpit. The instruments were: altimeter, inclinometer, clock, airspeed indicator, radiator coolant-temperature, rpm indicator and oil pressure indicator. The controls consisted of: arming lever for the Vickers gun (top centre of instrument panel), fuel tank pressure release valve, fuel tank pressurising hand pump, fuel system controls, starter magneto hand crank, radiator shutter control, tailplane incidence control, throttle and mixture control levers, rudder pedals and control column with gun trigger. Of course, there were also three other 'instruments', the Aldis sight and the ring-and-bead sight and the compass; the last item was inset at the trailing edge of the centre section.

A typical cockpit of late 1918

The cockpit of a typical RAF fighter of late 1918 would have all or most of the following equipment:

Ring and bead sight
Aldis sight
Signal pistol
Foster mounting for Lewis gun
Foster mounting unlocking pull ring
Arming (cocking) lever for Vickers gun or guns
Triggers on control column for Vickers and Lewis guns
Starter magneto hand crank
Ignition switches
Tail trimmer control
Engine controls
Sutton harness
Wickerwork seat
Oxygen supply mask
Oxygen supply control valve
Airspeed indicator (ASI)
Altimeter
Inclinometer
Oil pressure gauge
Fuel pressure gauge
CC Pump handle for the Constantinesco-Colley (C-C) interrupter gear
Fuel system selector cocks
Fuel pressure release cock
Fuel tank pressure pump handle
Compass

Typical single-seat fighter cockpit equipment c. *1918*

1. Foster mounting with 7.7mm Lewis gun.

2. Aldis optical sight.

3. Ring-and-bead sight.

4. Oxygen mask.

5. Cable ring to unlock gun on mounting.

6. Padded coaming.

7. Vickers 7.7mm gun with C-C interrupter system.

8. Cocking (arming) lever for gun.

9. Fuel tank pressure release valve.

10. Pump for pressurising C-C system.

11. Instrument panel with: indicators for airspeed, altitude, engine rpm, fuel tank pressure and oil pressure; cross-level bubble, compass, instrument lights and ignition switches.

12. Pump for pressurising the fuel tank.

13. Tail trim lever.

14. Sutton four-strap harness.

15. Control column with triggers for guns.

16. Very signal pistol.

17. Engine control levers.

18. Minimal wicker seat.

19. Rudder bar.

(Author)

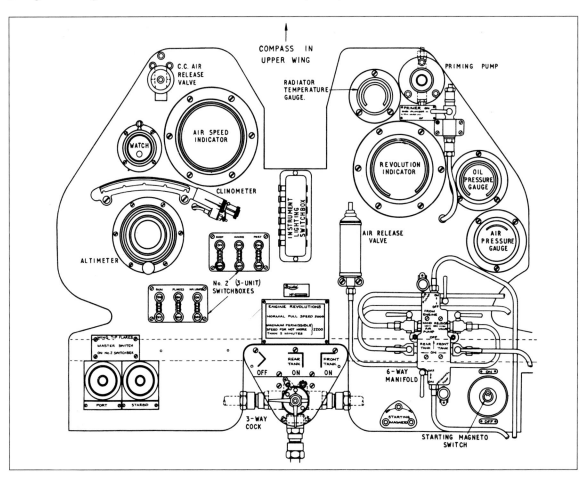

Opposite below: Bristol Fighter. Although this shows some post WWI standard equipment it can serve to illustrate a WWI cockpit. Points of interest: The cut out part at the top of the instrument panel for the single Vickers gun. The compass was housed in the trailing edge of the upper wing. Instrument lighting was fitted. The two rows of three switches (middle left) are for the electrically heated clothing circuits, the gun circuit and for the flares and navigation lights. Lower left are the wing tip landing flare selector buttons. The complicated plumbing and six-way manifold controls the pressurising air supply to the fuel tanks. Other than the clinometer there are no purpose designed 'blind' flying instruments.
(Dr J.M. Rolfe)

Wireless telegraphy

In 1914 voice, visual signals and wireless and telegraphic communication methods were an integral and vital part of the control systems for warships and armies at all levels. In contrast once a pilot or aircrew were airborne they were deprived, other than by ground signal panels, of contact with those on the ground.

Radio, or wireless to give it its original name, was evaluated for air-to-ground communication as early as 1907 by the British Army. Captain L. Evans of the Royal Engineers (RE) was one of the first to adapt a wireless telegraphy (WT) apparatus for airborne use. In the next year, 1908, Lt C.J. Aston RE conducted experiments with a WT receiver in a captive balloon and in the following year Captain H.P.T. Lefroy was appointed to command all WT experiments for communicating with aerial vehicles in the British Army. Similar experimental sets were tried by both the German and French air services.

By 1912 a BE 2 was equipped with an engine-driven generator for WT and Commander Samson, who did so much to advance naval avia-

AW FK 8. Instrument panel has been cut away on the left to accommodate the Vickers gun. The ammunition tank is mounted at the pilot's feet. The rpm indicator, in contrast to the other instruments, has black numerals and a pointer. The large black handle (lower right) is for hand pumping up the air pressure in the fuel tanks, the tank selector control for which is at the top centre of the panel. (Philip Jarrett)

tion, used a WT set in a Short floatplane to signal destroyers over a distance of ten miles. As with the Army, the Royal Navy recognised the potential importance of WT and placed a Lt Fitzmaurice in charge of WT in all naval aircraft.

Radio communication, in both the British and French air services, was limited in general to reconnaissance and artillery-spotting. In the winter of 1914–1915 the RFC expanded its 'wireless' flights in order to meet the demands of the artillery. The first airborne wireless sets were bulky and weighed about 75 lb. The usual two-seat observation aircraft two-seater did not have the performance or room for carrying both an observer and a radio set. Therefore, the lone pilot had to fly the aircraft, observe the fall of shells and operate the radio. Not until late 1915 did the RFC, for example, get the much lighter Sterling set, 20 lb, which could be accommodated in the cockpit along with the observer. In 1916 the RFC perfected its spotting technique for the artillery. Observers used an improved wireless telegraphic

apparatus with a variable Morse tone to avoid jamming by enemy transmitters or confusion among the many RFC spotter aircraft operating over the battlefield. WT equipment became a typical item of cockpit furniture.

Part of an RFC observer's cockpit equipment was the aerial winch. The aerial wire was generally about 150 to 250 feet in length. Instruction books of the time enjoin observers not to let the aerial down before the aircraft had gained sufficient height. Otherwise the wire could become entangled in trees, telephone wires and other ground features. The low engine power and low

RE 8 c. 1918. RAF Mk II compass in prominent position with instrument lighting switch panel below. The instruments have black markings and pointers on a white dial. The only 'flight' instrument is a cross level inclinometer. Unlike some other RFC/RAF aircraft, the forward-firing Vickers gun is mounted external to the cockpit on the port side. By leaning out the pilot could reach the breech cover of the gun in order to clear a stoppage.
(Philip Jarrett)

speed of the aircraft might not have been able to prevent a crash should the aerial snag something.

The first decade of heavier-than-air aviation and the increasing battle for naval supremacy in Europe encouraged greater interest in electronic systems. For example and as a precursor of future aviation developments and in particular cockpit instruments, Marconi in Italy described and Hulsmeyer in Germany demonstrated radar systems.

Radio-telephony (RT)

Yeates describes how after a dogfight over the Western Front in cloudy conditions his compass was spinning so much that he could not tell in which direction he had to fly to return to his aerodrome. He spotted another RFC aircraft but without any means of communication, such as RT, he did not know whether it was flying towards or away from enemy territory.[11] The Royal Flying Corps, for example, tried out radio-telephony (RT) from 1916 onward. By the end of WWI the

RAF was well in advance of RT developments in Germany

Radio communication provided the essential link which could eliminate the virtual isolation of a pilot when he was unsure of his position or of the tactical situation. In two-seater aircraft WT provided a means, albeit slow and uncertain, of keeping aircraft crews aware of what was happening to the troops on the ground. The latter sometimes advanced wearing polished metal identification plates on their backs to indicate how far they had advanced and to prevent being attacked by their own aircraft. These and ground signal panels provided information which could be communicated to headquarters using WT. However this was a slow process. By the time the coded signal had been passed along the chain of communication and command the tactical situa-

German air services Staaken four-engine bomber with enclosed cockpit. The noise level was so high that the crew could only communicate via electric visual signalling systems.
(Imrie)

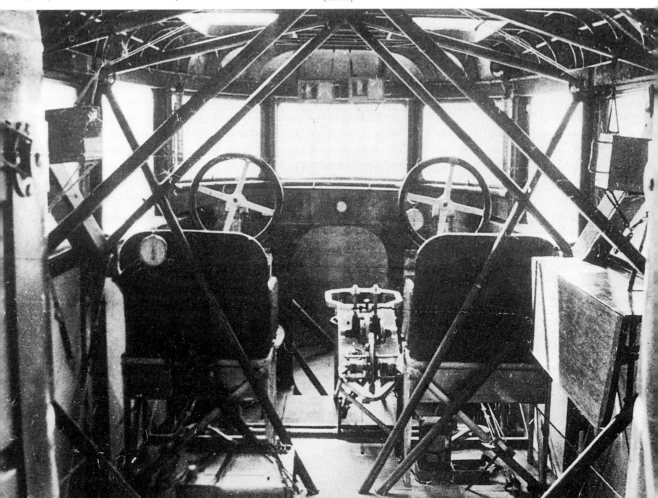

tion could have changed dramatically. A direct RT link of the type developed in the next few years would have revolutionised artillery spotting and tactical reporting from the air in WWI. (See Notes at the end of this chapter for a chronology of significant events in radio development.)

Hypoxia

At the end of WWI fighting aircraft were being flown as high as 20,000 feet and greater attention had to be paid to the adverse effects of high altitude on human physical performance. However, the considerable reduction of engine power above 20,000 feet precluded regular operations at extreme altitudes. Initial attempts to study the problem and devise solutions were confused by the variation among pilots and others of the subjective effects of oxygen starvation or hypoxia. Some flyers reported that they experienced no ill effects. Some suffered only after several flights above 12,000 feet. Although most pilots and others could overcome the effects of hypoxia for a short time above, say, 15,000 feet, routine flying in those conditions imposed a severe strain on the heart, induced tinnitus and deafness along with

DH 9 c. 1918. The mounting for the Vickers gun (not installed) is above the switch panel for the instrument lights. There are six small lights, three of which are set round the compass. Top centre is the fuel system tank selector. The hole in the windscreen is for an Aldis sight.
(Philip Jarrett)

the immediately observable symptoms of fatigue and nausea.

In 1917 German airship crews had the benefit of an oxygen supply for use above 15,000 feet. Although oxygen face masks were tried these tended to ice up and therefore airship crews preferred to use a pipe-stem mouthpiece. In 1917 German aircraft crews used gaseous oxygen. However in early 1918 a liquid oxygen apparatus was perfected. This was the Ahrendt u. Heylandt system that weighed only 15 lb when full and supplied 1,800 litres of gaseous oxygen.

In the last year of the war the RFC/RAF improved the methods of supplying oxygen for aircrew. Those responsible for considering the technologies that would be needed were the war to continue for another year or more realised that the air force which could attain the greatest heights would have the advantage.

Clothing

Just as the pilot or crew member is part of the cockpit as a subject so is clothing and special life support and comfort equipment. Fur and sheepskin-lined leather coats were typical garments for combating the cold of the open cockpit.

Looking aft at the pilot of a four-engine Staaken bomber c. 1918.
(Imrie)

What the best dressed German bomber pilot wore c. *1918. On the left can be seen the oxygen apparatus with tube leading to the pilot's mouthpiece. Unlike British multi-engine aircraft the principal or only pilot's position was on the left.*
(Imrie)

A leather or fur helmet plus scarf protected the head and neck. Field boots, worn by both German and British pilots, were elegant on the ground but did not prevent frozen legs and feet. In the RFC and particularly in the RNAS 'fug' boots were often worn. These were sheepskin-lined, cloth, thigh-high, boots similar to a fisherman's waders. It was even recommended that aircrew took a large hot potato along as a hand warmer.

Aircrew learnt the hard way by experience that many layers of close fitting clothing did not necessarily keep out the cold. Sidney Cotton of the RFC designed a one-piece flying overall which combined comfort, flexibility and warmth. This became the Sidcot suit and was copied by air-forces in all parts of the world and was still being supplied to RAF aircrew in WWII.

Electrically heated garments were available to the crews of the RAF's long-range night bombers. When the special garments worked they helped to mitigate the adverse effects of flying in air temperatures as low as minus 20°C. However, frequent failures of the insulation resulted in burns. Nevertheless the principle was established that electrically heated clothing was essential for flight in open cockpits above 20,000 feet in summer and above 10,000 feet in winter. Together electrically heated clothing and oxygen emphasise how the frontier of aviation in 1918 had been pushed far ahead of the limits of human ability and the aspirations of the Wright brothers.

Safety harness

Until about 1917 pilots were usually kept in their seat during violent manoeuvres by a lap strap. Sutton of the RFC devised a four-strap harness with a simple quick-release fastening. The Sutton harness became the standard for RFC, RNAS and RAF pilots. A similar four-strap harness was used in some French aircraft. Other crew members either had a lap strap or a 'monkey chain' to prevent them falling out. Moore[12] points out that at the end of WWI the admirable Sutton harness was forgotten by the RAF and only revived ten years later. The reason for this back-ward safety step lay possibly with the original object of the harness which was to keep a pilot firmly in his seat during a dog fight. The original

intention was not concerned with protecting the pilot in the event of a crash. There was disagree-ment among British pilots about keeping the strap secured or undone when making a forced landing. Some were concerned that in the event of a crash a waist strap or harness might prevent them escaping quickly from the wreck.

Meteorology

The airships of the Imperial German Navy and those of the RNAS required comprehensive meteorological information and forecasting. Airships were very dependent on acceptable flight conditions. Of those lost on both sides during WWI a significant proportion were casualties of storms. The RNAS established a number of meteorological stations whose data was collected and co-ordinated by radio.

The RFC, the French air force and the German air services in France initially were without weather information other than that issued by the different army headquarters. The RFC depended on the meteorologists of the Royal Engineers. The

Handley Page four-engine V1500 bomber of 1918. 'Right-hand drive'. With four V 12 engines and two magnetos for each bank of six cylinders there are 16 magneto switches on the instrument panel. The aperiodic compass is an improvement on those fitted to other aircraft. The large aileron/elevator wheel was needed to overcome the heavy control loads. In the bow is a Scarff ring mounting for the defensive gun.
(Handley Page)

F2 C 'Felixstowe' flying boat of the RAF c. 1918. Points of interest are: two sets of controls with principal pilot's position on the right and access forward to front cockpit in which can be seen the anchor windlass.
(Crown copyright)

service most reliant on meteorological data was the artillery. The shells of big long-range guns described trajectories whose zenith could be above 10,000 feet. The path of a shell could pass through layers of air each exhibiting differences in temperature, density and wind strength and direction. Meanwhile the airmen relied to a large extent on 'sniffing the air', studying the clouds and if the hills in the distance could be seen then it would rain; if they could not be seen then it was raining. Low cloud and rain usually prevented contact flying in support of the ground forces and spotting for the guns.

Meteorological flights

In 1918 the RFC/RAF had a 'Meteor' flight which made flights up to 15,000 feet for gathering data for the artillery and as an aid to weather forecasting. The observations included air temperature and humidity, visibility and the observation and photographing of cloud forms. The records make little mention of instruments for cloud-flying. One comment relating to the subject was: 'A pilot who specialises in the work can fly up through any thickness of cloud, while a pilot without experience of cloud-flying is liable to get into difficulties if he attempts to do so'.[13]

Chronology

Notes on British developments in radio communication before 1918. Similar developments were achieved by the French and German air services
1899   DF experiments for detecting ships.

1907	Scheller patent: 'To provide course information by beams'.
1907	Capt. L. Evans, 1st Wireless Co. RE, devised WT between aircraft and ground.
1908	Lt C.J. Aston RE, in a captive balloon, conducted air-to-ground WT experiments, followed by a free run in the balloon *Pegasus* equipped with a receiver.
1909	Capt. H.P.T. Lefroy RE O/C all WT experimental work.
1911	Airship BETA sent and received WT signals. Later Lefroy and G. de Havilland in a BE a/c tested WT installation. Not practicable to receive WT because of engine noise.
1912	Major Burle in a BE with engine-driven generator for WT.
1912	Cdr Samson RN in a Short a/c uses WT to signal destroyers at ten miles.
1912	Lt Raymond Fitzmaurice RN becomes O/C WT in naval a/c.
1913	In RNAS WT in most a/c. Transmission of meteorological charts so that stations and a/c could receive weather reports.
1914	Cat's whisker and crystal receiver with spark-gap transmitter used by No 4 Squadron RFC for artillery spotting sorties.
1914–16	Round of Marconi develops 'Round' telephone for RT.
1915	Prince system of RT demonstrated to RFC staff at end of year. Trenchard convinced of value of RT and encourages development of RT set with one mile range and antennae limited to 150 ft. RT known as wireless telephony.
1915	RFC Experimental Wireless Section demonstrated RT. Difficulties with microphones: either too sensitive or too insensitive for airborne use.
1917	RT introduced experimentally into two squadrons followed by further installations.

A Round Prince set of 1915 resurrected and installed in a BE 2e

Trials emphasised need for close fitting pilot's helmet and drawback of trailing aerial.

Air-to-air RT achieved.

It is interesting to note that the experiments emphasised the need for close fitting helmets for the pilots (PPO342). RT was not fully developed for fighter aircraft until 1918.

| 1918 | In June 141 Squadron Bristol Fighters equipped with RT to work with Defence Operations Room as part of UK Home Defence system. |
| 1918 | Three-beacon WT/DF system developed for HP O/400 and HP 1500 long-range operations. Long-range Type 7 receiver and Mk II TX used by several RAF squadrons for passing reports during night sorties. |

Notes

1. Jones, H.A. *The War In The Air 1914–1918* Vol II p120. Oxford, Clarendon 1922–1934
2. Grennell-Milne, D. (1933) *Wind in the Wires*, p. 113 Hurst & Blackett.
3. PRO AIR 1/756/204/4/91
4. Jones, H.A. op cit p. 27
5. Penrose, H. *The Great War and Armistice 1915–1919*, p. 97. Putnam
6. Ibid. p 191
7. Bridgeman & Stewart (1938) *The Clouds Remember*. Gale & Polden. *Winged Victory* published in 1934
8. Freddette, (1966) *The First Battle of Britain*, p. 179 Cassell.
9. Jones, H.A. *The War in the Air 1914–1918*, Vol II p. 156. Oxford, Clarendon 1922–1937
10. Penrose op cit p 210
11. Yeates, V.M. (1934) *Winged Victory*, Jonathan Cape
12. Moore, W.G. (1963) *Early Bird*, p. 135. Putnam
13. Haslam, Group Captain the Revd J.A.G. Letter to author.

CHAPTER TWO

1919 – 1930

The end of the Great War (WWI) came just as military aviation was about to enter a new phase. Fighter performance was significantly better than in 1914 and the potential of the bomber had been proved. Higher fighting altitudes encouraged the development of oxygen systems and the parachute was about to become a standard item of equipment.

In 1919 France, the United States and Britain were free to pursue civil as well as military aviation. Air forces had to make do with existing aircraft as much as possible. Civil airlines started up by buying surplus war machines or bombers adapted to carry passengers. In Germany civil aviation was allowed but nothing pertaining to the development and warlike use of military aircraft was permitted under the terms of the Versailles Treaty.

The end of the war meant a sudden stop to aircraft production and a review of research projects. The latter, up to then, had virtually unlimited resources; but in peace other matters took priority. Therefore many technological advances that might have been made, say, in 1919 or 1920 were delayed for another ten years. Of course, for aviation as a whole the sudden removal of Germany as a belligerent also eliminated a source of aviation research and development. It would be another ten years before German technology, particularly engines and cockpit equipment, such as instruments and radio, would contribute to the overall technology of military aviation.

Radial engine

The rotary engine was being displaced by the radial: the former having reached the upper limit of power. The radial type would have entered service earlier with the Allied powers had there not been serious development problems to be overcome. Its importance to the history of the cockpit is the improvement it afforded the pilot who no longer had to breathe castor oil-laden fumes. Contemporary accounts of flying rotary-engine machines frequently mention the effect castor oil had on the stomach. The oil flung back from the engine also got onto the pilot's goggles and onto the forward lens of the Aldis sight.

The new breed of engines developed, on average, 400 hp. They were more reliable than the earlier types and less prone to in-flight fires. The lessons of war were applied to engine installation and the fire-retarding bulkhead between cockpit and engine became a standard feature.

Radio telephone

Cockpits in general were acquiring more instruments and controls. Wireless apparatus was no longer an experiment and confined to artillery spotting tasks. The radio telephone was in use and was about to become the principal means of communication between ground and air and between air and ground. No longer would interceptor pilots have to depend on visual ground-based signals, in the form of white panels, white arrows or patterns of lights to indicate the position of the enemy. By the end of the war the German air services had developed electric signal panels flush with the airfield surface for informing pilots of the landing conditions

In 1919 some RAF reconnaissance aircraft were equipped with the Type 21 transmitter and receiver for communication with the Type 57 ground radio station. The Mk III RT receiver and No 12 amplifier were used for the training of pilots in the use of RT for formation flying and for reconnaissance reporting. In London in August of that year a radio telephone link was demonstrated for the benefit of members of both Houses between an RAF aircraft and the Palace of Westminster. In 1921 Instone's civil airliners were fitted with RT for the London–Paris service but RAF bombers were yet to be equipped with RT as a squadron standard.

The technology of radio aids to navigation and landings were advanced in the 1920s. Although these were intended in the first place to improve the safety and regularity of civil airline operations they were also applicable to air force operations. Both France and the air services of the USA kept their eyes on these developments which in the next ten years were to make significant changes to cockpit equipment. In 1927 Dunmore & Engel in the USA patented the four-course, radio range and radio navigational beacons were being introduced for airways in USA. The air staff in the UK were interested but with reservations because they did not want an air force dependent on fixed ground systems such as radio beams. Instead they concentrated on the development of radio direction finding (DF). An aircraft DF set in those years usually had to be attended to by a radio

operator and was not directly under the control of the pilot. By 1930 radio aids to navigation and landing were developed in Germany that would match the technology of other countries.

Despite these wonders of modern electronic technology in the 1920s, the RAF continued to rely on visual signal panels on the ground and dropping message bags for communication with the Army. As late as 1933, if not later, Wapiti squadrons operating with the Army during the many skirmishes with the tribesmen of the North West Frontier of India received information from the ground by means of the Popham Panel. White canvas strips of various sizes and shapes could be

Vickers Vimy bomber c. 1919. Engine instruments are mounted on the inboard side of each nacelle. This method of simplifying wiring and pipework was used for many types of aircraft in the 1920s and 1930s.
(Vickers)

Vickers Vimy. Note the brass 'domestic' switches for the four ignition systems and the few instruments; of which only one, an inclinometer, provides some indication of aircraft attitude. Bottom right is the throttle lever controlling both engines simultaneously. Turning the large knob on top of the lever applied differential engine control.
(Vickers)

laid out in accordance with a code book. An Army post or platoon was able to lay out simple messages such as: 'We are under attack from the north' or 'Send reinforcements'. A reassuring reply would be written out on the pilot's or air gunner's knee pad and enclosed in a weighted message bag. This was then dropped close to the troops on the ground.

In 1925 the first UK autopilot patent (Meredith & Cook) was granted but it would be a few more years before RAF bomber aircraft cockpits included the controls for an autopilot. In 1927 Lindbergh flew the Atlantic using an earth inductor compass as a primary navigational aid and Francis Chichester made an epic solo flight from New Zealand to Australia via Lord Howe Island using the sun line navigational technique to avoid missing the tiny island. These are just some of the technical advances against which the fighting cockpit was developing. Improving the accuracy of navigation was of great importance for long-range bombing sorties of which few had

much experience. The Germans had advanced long-range navigational techniques when operating Shutte Lanz and Zeppelin dirigibles against targets in France and Britain. Similarly the RNAS/RAF had operated long-range flying boats that depended for navigational accuracy on two or more ground stations which provided a DF fix. Previously the crew of the larger types of aircraft was made up of pilots, observers and gunners. Now a wireless operator was added along with a cockpit or space for his equipment.

Irvin parachute

A major advance in safety occurred in 1919 when

Leslie Irvin proved the effectiveness of his back-pack type parachute. This had the now familiar D ring which when pulled released the canopy from the pack. He made his first jump with the new parachute on 28 April 1919. The US Army Air Service was impressed and ordered three hundred. In July of the same year the air service evaluated the Calthrop Guardian Angel attached-type parachute but decided it was unsuitable and even more so when the RAF officer demonstrating the parachute was killed because it became entangled with the aircraft and failed under the load.[1] Previously the Air Service had evaluated the German Heinicke parachute but was contemptuous of its design and performance although it had saved many aircrew lives in the last year of the war.

In the meantime RAF Martlesham Heath, later the Aeroplane & Armament Experimental Establishment (A&AEE), experimented with different types of parachute including the Calthrop Guardian Angel. Among the ideas tested was the arrangement whereby the parachute was stowed under the rear cockpit and attached to the user by an external wire. However, none was successful and in December 1924 the RAF adopted the Irvin parachute.

Vickers Virginia bomber with open gunners' cockpits.
(Smiths Industries Archives)

Gun-aiming systems

Other standard, as opposed to experimental, cockpit equipment of this period did not include much advance in gun-aiming systems. Although the optical, collimated, reflector sight was available to the German air services in 1918 it remained only a possible alternative to the collimated Aldis or to the ring-and-bead. During WWI fighter pilots attempting to intercept bombers and airships at night were provided with illuminated sights such as the Hutton and the Neame used by the RFC and RNAS. Aiming at night would continue to be a problem even in WWII. In Britain, Bar & Stroud designed their GJ3 reflector sight in 1924 for the guns of bombers. Perhaps the most important legacy of WWI to all the world's air forces were the fuselage, synchronised, guns. These were still being mounted so as to be within reach of the pilot so that the stoppages to which they were prone could be dealt with.

Open cockpits

The shape and position of the cockpit remained very much as they had been in 1918 for the next fifteen years. The enclosed cockpit was rare even though aircraft designers sometimes provided an enclosure for a prototype but this was often disliked by pilots and removed. Attitude instrument

Vickers Vimy cockpit from an unusual angle; hence the
photographer's legs. Typical RAF 'right-hand drive' cockpit of
the 1920s.
(Vickers)

development was slow and the bubble-in-glass inclinometer remained the primary indication of attitude in most aircraft for the next ten years. Pilots in general preferred to rely on the 'wind-on-the-cheek' as an indicator of side slip in a turn. Although there was some improvement in arcs of vision from the cockpit the majority of pilots had to share their forward view with that of the upper wing and its struts. Obviously the monoplane conferred a good all-round view for the pilot but reluctance by some designers to change from a wire braced structure to cantilever wings retarded its wholesale introduction as an alternative to the biplane.

Approaching the stratosphere

On 27 February 1920 Major Schroeder of the US Air Service became the first man to exceed 30,000 feet in an aircraft. The flight is also of significance to the history of the cockpit because the aircraft's engine was turbo-supercharged. From that flight onward turbo-supercharging, using the engine exhaust, was advanced in the USA year by year with the result that flight at altitudes above 30,000 feet became the accepted design requirement for many American military aircraft. As we have seen in WWI, although the machine might survive at extreme altitudes the human crew had to be protected from both the extreme cold and the rarefied air. The development of life support equipment

became as important as the development of engines able to maintain their power at high altitudes. Anticipating the time when flight at extreme altitudes would be an essential part of air force operations the United States commissioned a high altitude chamber at the Mineola NY medical research laboratory in 1918. By 1921 a Packard-Le Pere with an exhaust-turbine driven supercharger flown by Lt McReady of the Air Corps climbed to 34,000 feet. This was to be one of a number of experimental high altitude flights in America that advanced the technologies of engine supercharging, high altitude clothing and eventually pressurised cabins.

As military aviation advanced in the 1920s in technology, if not in numbers of aircraft, the medical aspects of flying became of increasing importance. Although part of civil aviation, the 'round the pylons' air races, popular in the USA, anticipated the high G effects to which fighter pilots would be subjected as aircraft performance advanced. In a near vertical bank round a pylon a racing pilot could experience a blackout as the blood was forced towards his feet by the 4G or more of the turn. In earlier years few pilots had been seriously affected by G. If they had, their aircraft was about to suffer severe structural failure.

Where are they?

Since the 1930s fighter pilots have been directed through RT toward their target by a controller on the ground. But in the 1920s a fighter pilot, even when using RT, had no precise guidance from the ground and therefore needed a good all-round view when searching for the enemy. The structural members of an enclosed cockpit only added to the 'forest' of interplane struts and rigging wires. Another drawback to an enclosed position was the difficulty it presented when using arm signals to other pilots in a formation. The open cockpit of the 1928 Boeing P-12 biplane of the US Navy could be used to demonstrate a 'hands-off' characteristic of the aircraft. As one P-12 pilot commented: 'Poke your left hand out, she'll do a nice turn to the left'. Did this characteristic limit the use of hand signals? In the US Navy information about speed, course and altitude was some-

41

times conveyed from the leader of a formation of two-seat aircraft to the others in the formation by means of alphanumerics chalked on a small blackboard.

The open cockpit was retained for fighter and two-seat aircraft by most air forces well into the mid-1930s. In the 1920s there were only a few experimental aircraft with a completely enclosed pilot's place. Besides the need for a good all-round view the open cockpit was preferred for other reasons. For example, in some aircraft types the fumes from the engine could be lethal. Also, because many pilots enjoyed driving fast cars, most of which were open top, it was the macho thing to do the same in an aircraft. Pilots of those air forces that operated flying boats, such as the French and US navies and the RAF, had to suffer the effects of the spray thrown up when on the water. The open cockpits gave little protection against waves breaking over the bow or spray picked up by the propellers and blown forward when taxying downwind.

Cockpit design in the 1920s

Cockpit designers in the 1920s had to solve two basic and conflicting requirements. These had been present in the first decade but had not been so critical. One, they had to position cockpit equipment in such a way as to simplify the pilot's many tasks; tasks that had increased with the increase in aircraft systems and aircraft potential. Two, they wanted, as they always would, to simplify the mechanical linkages which connected cockpit controls to the different aircraft systems and equipment; such as throttle and mixture levers to the engine, fuel system control cocks and levers to the actual fuel cocks, and so on.

As could happen in cockpit design, practical

Avro Tutor: brass 'domestic' double ignition switch; starting magneto switch and the then new turn and slip indicator alongside a fore-and-aft inclinometer. The mouthpiece of the Gosport tube to the rear cockpit is on the right. This is representative of British trainer cockpits c. 1930.
(British Aerospace)

considerations dictated compromises. Obviously, the primary flight controls of stick and rudder bar had to be within reach of the pilot's hands and feet. However, other controls were sometimes positioned in locations that required the pilot to reach and grope. Awkward control positions and operation were the result of the designer having to avoid expensive and complex control linkages. The increasing use of electrical systems provided some improvement in overall cockpit design. Electrical wiring cables could be laid round, through and across other items in order to reach the switches. Unfortunately there were many examples of cockpits in which controls and instruments and switches had been 'tossed in' to land where they might.

A frequent criticism of the cockpits of aircraft submitted to the A&AEE at Martlesham Heath for type approval in the 1920s was the lack of space for a pilot wearing full flying kit and parachute. This may have been the result of manufacturers not being in touch with actual service flying conditions and dimensioning the cockpit around an unclothed manikin. In one aircraft submitted for approval the test pilot found that he could not get out of the seat without first undoing the straps of the parachute harness. The report on another aircraft criticised the flight controls, which were heavy at all speeds, and went on to comment on the narrowness of the cockpit, the badly positioned controls and the plate glass windscreen which could splinter in a crash.[2]

If pilots' cockpits were criticised for being cramped and having badly positioned controls, the gunners' cockpits were criticised for exposing the occupant to extreme cold and the blast of the slipstream which could lift goggles off the face, making it very difficult for the gunner to train the gun on the beam.

Ignition switches

The mention of switches introduces the British stereotype of 'up' for 'on' and 'down' for 'off' ignition control. This is opposite to a domestic light switch. The reason for the apparent anomaly is that the ignition switch does not directly 'switch' on the circuit. When the switch is up and therefore 'on' the connection to earth (ground) is cut.

In the down 'off' position the self-contained magneto system is earthed (grounded) and therefore safe. Hence the 'Switches off?' call before the propeller is pulled round preparatory to starting the engine. This 'up' for 'on' has been applied to other electrical systems in both civil and military aircraft and in at least one well known make of car. However, in American and German aircraft in particular the ignition switches were usually grouped in one selector switch that provided 'all off', left magneto on, right magneto on, or both on.

Following a number of crashes at RAF air-to-ground firing ranges attention focused on the ignition switches. As a pilot pulled the aircraft up after diving on the target the engine would cut. Those pilots who survived found it hard to believe that they had moved the ignition switches at such a critical point. Eventually an investigation showed that as an aircraft was pulled out of a dive attack the ignition switches were being moved down and 'off' by the G force of the pull out.

In the majority of cockpits of the previous decade the pilot's heels touched the floor and there were few hidden corners into which tools and rubbish could lurk. The bigger engines of the 1920s required deeper fuselages so that there was often space beneath the pilot's feet and seat. Rubbish of all kinds accumulated below until negative G was applied. Then a rain of dried mud, lost screwdrivers, spanners and other odds and ends fell out of the 'bilges' and past the pilot's head.

In the air forces of these years there were numerous incidents and accidents caused by loose objects falling into control cables, rods and levers. Sometimes a forgotten spanner would fall among the control linkages and completely jam the system. Since the earliest days of flight an essential pre-take-off drill has been a careful check of the correct and free movement of the controls. There have been many examples of incorrectly rigged controls. Some accidents have been caused because the pilot failed to check that the control locks had been removed. These locks prevented the control surfaces being banged about by the wind when the aircraft was parked. Control locks have often been a 'time bomb' waiting to destroy a careless crew. Twenty years on lives would still be lost from this cause. In one example a pilot of a four-engine bomber took off without noticing that the aileron locking device was still attached to the controls. Examination of the wreckage revealed that the crew had made desperate attempts to smash the lock.

Instrument flight

In the previous chapter mention was made of cloud-flying in the RFC/RAF in 1918. When the meteorological flights reformed after WWI the RAF pilots still flew in cloud without the benefit of any specialised instrumentation. Essentially, they had only an airspeed indicator, compass and cross level inclinometer with which to avoid 'falling out' of the clouds upside down in a 'graveyard' spiral At the time a number of 'blind' flying instruments were under development; such as the Darwin Static Turn Indicator and gyro-based attitude indicators. However none was successful.

In the UK W.E.P. Johnson was one of the pilots in the 1920s who made a thorough study of the ways in which a pilot reacts to sensations of

An early version of the Sperry artificial horizon. This along with the directional gyro and the turn and bank indicator enabled pilots to stay the right way up and fly in cloud without losing control.
(Sperry Gyroscope Co.)

aircraft movement when flying 'blind'. His research showed that even among the experienced pilots, none could fly in cloud or under the 'hood' without getting into a spin within a few minutes. Eight minutes was the maximum. The problem was one of perceived acceleration forces on the part of a pilot attempting to maintain steady flight without a visible horizon. When the pilot attempted to stop a spin the accelerating forces applied to the semi-circular canals in his ears produced a sensation of entering another spin but in the opposite direction to the first even though the aircraft may have stopped spinning. Johnson emphasised the value of the gyro-based turn indicators that were being introduced into service aircraft. The RAF's Central Flying School produced a curriculum based on the precept that pilots had to ignore 'seat of the pants' sensations when flying with no visible horizon. In 1925 the Farman School of Flying near Paris introduced the extendible hood for the pupil's cockpit. This enabled a pilot to perfect his 'blind' flying skill under realistic conditions of flight.

In 1928 the Hawker Tomtit trainer for the RAF had an extendible hood for the pupil's cockpit, and a Reid & Sigrist instrument panel for 'blind' flying. Reid & Sigrist developed many types of flight instruments and this included the recently developed turn and bank indicator by which a pilot could effect a perfectly co-ordinated turn. That is a turn in which the aircraft is banked at an angle at which it neither slips inward or slips outward. Despite the advances made in instrumentation the financial restrictions under which the RAF had to live in the 1920s and early 1930s meant that turn and bank indicators were in short supply. Even some first-line fighter aircraft, such as the Bristol Bulldogs, were not equipped with turn and bank indicators.

Group Captain The Reverend J.A.G. Haslam's[3] recollections of 'met' flying from RAF Andover in 1920–22 provide an insight into the typical cockpit of the era and the problems faced by pilots. He describes how he had to spend at least half an hour above the maximum 10,000 feet height then permitted for flying without oxygen equipment. The cockpits were open and the only heating was what came back from the engine. In the Sopwith Snipe, with its air-cooled rotary

Pilots' Cockpit of Vickers "Vixen" Military Two Seater.

engine, it was uncomfortably cold. In the Bristol Fighter, with a water-cooled engine, it was also cold in the cockpit. The main problem was to keep the engine from getting too cold when descending from high altitude. He used to bring the nose of the aircraft well up and fly nearly stalled on a quarter-throttle. This technique kept the engine warm and a rate of descent about the same as that of a normal glide. With no heated clothing provided (presumably because of a lack of electrical power) his hands became so cold that writing down meteorological observations was difficult.

Another problem recalled by Haslam and typical of the RAF of those years, was the lack of radio communication with the ground from which to obtain navigational assistance. With little time in which to spare from controlling the aircraft and recording observations and knowing only the wind speed and direction that had existed on the ground at the start of the flight, the pilot had to

Two-seat, multi-purpose, Vickers Vixen c. 1923. At the top of the instrument panel is a Reid, gyro-based, turn control indicator. Lights around the periphery and in a row below an integral airspeed indicator, show turn rate and slip. (Vickers)

apply careful mental dead reckoning calculations that would ensure a safe descent down through cloud and close to the airfield.

Instrument development in North America

In the United States after WWI the reaction against war stifled the fledgling air services of the US Army. In France during the war the Americans had largely had to use French and British equipment. For example, de Havilland aircraft were constructed in North America in the last year of the war. This meant that cockpit equipment was also non-American and for another five or more years instrument development in North America was slow.

William Ocker of the Air Corps researched the problems of maintaining control of an aircraft when the horizon was invisible. He made similar studies to those of Johnson of the RAF. One of his contributions to flight safety was a simulator for demonstrating to pilots that they had to rely on their instruments and not on their perceived sensations of aircraft movement. He taught the technique of concentrating on the needle and ball of the turn and slip indicator and on airspeed.

In the USA in 1929, Kollsman and Sperry instruments enabled Lt Doolittle in a Consolidated two-seat biplane to take off, complete a circuit of the airfield and land the aircraft back at the starting point without being able to see out of the cockpit. From the special set of instruments developed for that important flight in the history of flying evolved a succession of better and better 'blind flying' instruments. Parallel work in Britain, notably by W.E.P. Johnston and Reid and Sigrist, who developed the turn and bank indicator, led eventually to the RAF's Basic Six instrument panel that included: altimeter, airspeed, turn and slip and vertical speed indicators and Sperry artificial horizon and gyro heading indicators. (In the first four decades of British aviation the vertical speed indicator was usually called the Rate of Climb and Descent.)

The Wimperis course-setting bomb sight, used by the RAF in the last year of WWI, was the subject of a succession of improvements during the 1920s and 1930s. However, accurate and consistent bomb-aiming would remain an elusive goal until the 1940s. There were still too many unknown factors involved in steering an aircraft on a track relative to the target: uncertain information on wind direction and strength at different altitudes; often inadequate means whereby the bomb-aimer directed the pilot; and inconsistent and sometimes unknown bomb ballistics. The Goertz sights used in German bombers during the war had advanced optics that put them ahead of French, British or American equipment. The optical system included a 5:1 magnification, a bubble to indicate aircraft attitude and a remote indicator at the pilot's position. Following the introduction of the compensating sights, such as the Wimperis and the Goertz, a prone or kneeling position became

the usual for the bomb-aimer. In the USA scientists applied themselves to developing semi-automatic bomb sights, such as the Sperry and the Norden.

Throughout the 1920s and 30s patent applications for weapon, bomb and torpedo-aiming proliferated. But there appears to be little relationship between the intellectual exercises of the innovators and the operational requirements of air forces. The inaccuracies associated with bombing from level flight encouraged the development of the dive-bombing technique which in turn required a good view over the nose of single-engine aircraft and dedicated aiming sights.

Automatic pilots

During the 1920s inventors, scientists and pilots made numerous attempts to develop automatic flight controls. In 1913 Sperry had demonstrated his gyro-based stabilising system. War intervened and the subject was put aside. The mental and physical strain imposed on the pilots who made the pioneering long-distance flights was immense. Reading the accounts of Alcock and Brown's crossing of the Atlantic and Smith's 11,000-mile flight from the UK to Australia emphasises how difficult their aircraft were to control. The need for devices which would assist a pilot to control an aircraft was a high priority target.

A parallel line of research, with similar control problems to be solved, was concerned with finding ways to land aircraft safely in low visibility. In Britain the RAE experimented with a technique in which a Vickers Vimy was flown along the approach-to-landing path at a steady speed and trimmed tail heavy in the touch-down attitude. A 'ground proximity' indicator, consisting of a weight on the end of a line, suspended a fixed distance below the aircraft. When the weight touched the ground an observer, with his hand on the line, signalled the pilot who then released the controls to allow the aircraft to land itself.

Other influences

The design and equipment of the average military aircraft cockpit of the 1920s exhibited numerous faults and shortcomings, including the lack of consideration given by designers to the needs of the human occupant. Nevertheless they reflected the standards of the time. For example, neither the automobile nor the ship had control positions based on sound ergonomic design standards. In other forms of transport and in industry as a whole, particularly in process and manufacturing plants, control positions were little removed from the poor standards of Victorian times. At the majority of control positions at sea, on land, in mines and production plants drivers and operators were expected to stretch and wrestle with badly designed controls and share their view of the instruments with machinery and clouds of steam and gases. These, to us, generally unaccept-

able control interfaces were not deliberate actions on the part of designers and management. Few knew any better. We have to remember that in the 1920s and in earlier decades, our modern sciences of human factors and ergonomics were virtually unknown outside a narrow circle of academics. Therefore aircrews did not expect anything different and designers were often not aware of the problems or the alternatives.

Notes

1. Robinson, D.H. (1973) *The Dangerous Sky*, p. 144. Foulis.
2. Mason, T. (1993) *British Flight Testing,* Putnam.
3. Haslam, Group Captain the Revd J.A.G., correspondence with the author.

CHAPTER THREE

1930 – 1939

The march back to war

The decade before WWII might be called the 'march back to war'. It was also the decade in which the all-metal monoplane came to dominate the thoughts of the different air staffs among the potential warring nations. It was also the decade when the multi-engine bomber superseded the single-engine. These were the years when increasing speed encouraged greater enclosure of crew positions and powered gun mountings.

Of course, the change from the two-cockpit, single-engine, 'multi-role combat' biplane did not happen overnight. The twin restraints of limited money and a conservative approach to new technologies, particularly in Britain, resulted in the retention of the biplane for both fighters and bombers long after its 'use-by' date. At the same time cockpit equipment changed little and then only slowly from existing type to new types of aircraft.

This is the place for a comment on the terms 'fighter' and 'bomber' in relation to the cockpit. The former is usually used for an aircraft whose primary function is the destruction of the enemy's aircraft in the air. The latter usually applies to an aircraft used for destroying the enemy's ground-based resources. Air staff specifications and the ingenuity of designers have produced many aircraft types able to perform a number of different tasks. This is why it may be better, when discussing cockpits, to classify aircraft under the following:'

Having only one, single-seat, cockpit.

Having two or more single-seat cockpits in tandem.

Having pilots' cockpits and crew positions connected by a gang- or crawlway.

Having only one, two-seat, side-by-side cockpit.

The proposed classification is independent of the number of engines. For example, the United States Army Air Corps (USAAC) in the 1930s operated a number of bombers in which there were single-seat isolated cockpits; the twin-engine Martin bombers for example. In WWI a typical multi-engine bomber had an open pilot's cockpit with a gangway forward to the bow position occupied by the observer/gunner/bomb-aimer. In the late 1930s there were some French bombers with two separated pilots' positions. Presumably, they were set apart to improve survivability in the event of damage by enemy action.

For the convenience of the designer

Although not exclusive to this decade, placing equipment where it was convenient to the designer rather than in the best position for the pilot was a common feature of British aircraft. Control levers, wheels, knobs and switches were often positioned in the cockpit so as to simplify the layout of their associated rods and cables, shafts and electric wiring. The fact that the pilot had to contort and stretch his limbs in order to reach and operate a particular lever or switch was of secondary consideration.

The convenience of the designer and the lack of knowledge other than a superficial understanding of what we now know as ergonomics, contributed to some appalling cockpits. The RAF was particularly cursed by this failing and had to operate a number of aircraft types with badly arranged cockpits. These will be described later. German aircraft of the 1930s usually had a better detailed design of instruments and controls but the overall arrangement often sacrificed good instrument positions, as will be described, to the pilot's forward and downward views. American cockpits of the era were little better: however the greater use of electrically-operated systems contributed to tidier cockpits. Electrical wiring could be arranged to go round corners more easily than pipes and rods and cables and therefore the designer could group the various switches.

In the 1930s very little was written about the relationship between the controls and instruments of the cockpit and the pilot. The many different cockpits occupied by pilots reflected more or less the current level of thought on the subject. As with airframes and engines and other equipment, cockpits and their fittings were not necessarily the best available. Specifications issued three or four years before a new aircraft type entered squadron service predicated instruments and controls available at the time the specification was issued. Those items of cockpit which were modern were usually modifications introduced after the aircraft had entered service. For example: although the RAF was to have the collimated reflector gunsight as standard equipment, few of the Hurricanes or other fighters were equipped with it because of production delays. Initially they had to make do with the long-established ring-and-bead.

Gloster Gladiator fighter c. 1939. This illustrates the pilot's view wooded by wings and cabane.
(Peter Ottery)

Among pilots, particularly those who flew single-seat monoplane aircraft, was the continuing reluctance to be in a fully enclosed cockpit. They always wanted to be able to see without obstruction in all directions; even though the view was far less wooded than in a biplane. This is one reason why a number of new monoplane fighters had open cockpits, even though others gained a reduction in drag by having an enclosed pilot's place. The tradition of the need to 'feel the wind on the cheek' died hard and, as mentioned, lethal engine exhaust gas might gather in a completely enclosed cockpit.

Hot suits

Electrically heated flying clothing was essential in the open cockpit aircraft of the era. A typical heated suit consisted of trousers, jacket, gloves and boots. The suit was connected to the electrical supply through a cable and plug-in socket. Test pilot J.F. Quill OBE recalls that the suits were usually very reliable although sometimes a single glove finger or a whole boot would go open

circuit, making the member very uncomfortable. On one occasion a fault started the kapok lining of the suit smouldering. The pilot had to make a rapid descent, land in a field and strip off the smouldering suit.

In the mid-1930s the RAF's first-line fighter technology and the cockpit in particular were represented by the Hawker Fury II biplane with only two guns. The instruments and equipment of the cockpit were not much in advance of those in the cockpits of 1918. The Fury II and its earlier marks, had an open cockpit with a diminutive windscreen descended directly from fighters of WWI. It perpetuated the twin synchronised Vickers 7.7mm gun arrangement of its predecessors; with the gun breaches accessible to the pilot so that he could deal with stoppages. Significant items of equipment missing on a Fury in 1936 were navigation lights and landing lamps. Night flying was not a major part of a Fury pilot's life. When the Fury was conceived in 1929 electrical systems were limited in capacity and few single-engine aircraft had engine-driven generators.

The Fury was designed to a specification which demanded both speed and a good rate of climb, therefore endurance had to be sacrificed. With a range of only 300 miles from its 50 gallons of fuel it had a limited radius of action. In 1936 fighter tactics were still pre-radar. The defence of London, for example, depended on visual and aural tracking of enemy bombers from the ground. In the air the target had to be visually spotted by the pilot and therefore he preferred an open to a closed cockpit. The Fury II took nearly ten minutes to reach 20,000 feet. In that time an attacker could advance 30 miles. With only a small speed margin over a typical bomber a stern chase was unlikely to succeed. This factor and the limited aircraft performance and the difficulties of controlling fighters in general during air exercises forced the development of radar. It also presaged the time when interceptor fighters would be integrated completely with the information and control net.

Wireless operator's cockpit

The increasing range of aircraft and their ability to operate in cloud and at night encouraged development of better radio equipment for communication and navigation. With the general increase in the size of bombers, space was found for a dedicated wireless operator's position. In the USA and Germany significant advances were made in the 1930s in radio transmitters and receivers, along with remote controls, which would prove to be in advance of those in British aircraft when WWII started. Wireless operators in RAF Bomber and Coastal Commands were still using radio transmitters and receivers whose designs were not much in advance of those of 1918. For example, the tuning of both transmitter and receiver within different frequency bands required the use of plug-in coils. Changing to another band of frequencies took time: even longer if the tuning coils of the type 1082/1083 sets were jammed in position by expansion or frozen in their sockets.

Defendable bombers

Since the end of WWI air forces had persisted with the concept of the defendable bomber. There

The three gunners' positions in the HP Heyford were as exposed as those of a WWI bomber.
(Smiths Industries Archives)

was an alternative: the undefended bomber, that relied on high speed to avoid both pursuit and destruction. The two-seat in tandem layout of WWI was the norm for single-engine bombers and they were expected to be defended by a gunner with one or two flexibly mounted machine-guns. The open gunner's cockpit was also applied to multi-engine bombers. If intercepted by fighters then they were expected to 'fight it out'.

Enclosed gun positions

It had been obvious for some years that open cockpit mountings for manually trained guns were rendered useless because of the rush of air. Increasing speeds encouraged the development of power-assisted or fully powered gun mountings. This is where in the history of the cockpit we find a significant divergence of opinion. In Britain the future was recognised as being with the powered-mounting or the completely enclosed power-operated gun turret. In Germany and the United States less attention was given to power assistance for the air gunner. In contrast all future RAF bombers and ocean patrol aircraft, provided there was space available, would be defended by guns in power-operated turrets. The Barnes Wallis 'windscreen' casemate installations, as in the early Wellingtons, were frequently called 'turrets' even though only the guns and sights moved, not the complete enclosure. Among the new generation of bombers for the RAF in the mid-1930s was the Hampden. The athwartship dimensions of the narrow fuselage left little room in which the crew could turn around and even less for the installation of power-operated gun turrets. Hitherto the space needed for the crew had dictated fuselage dimensions, now it was the turret which might dictate the minimum acceptable cross-section at the nose and tail. The prototype Vickers Wellington's nose and tail were too small to accommodate a turret.

Strength in numbers

The gun-defended bomber concept depended for its effectiveness on formation flying so that each aircraft could bring cross-fire to bear on any fighters attempting to attack. This form of defence was employed in WWI. However any bomber that failed to keep up with the formation was doomed. In the mid-1930s the RAF continued to place great faith in daylight formations for bombers and therefore encouraged the development of power-operated, multi-gun turrets.[1] In 1936 the RAF was well committed to the concept of the defendable bomber as was the USAAC and the French air force. The German air force did not at that time envisage operations in which bombers penetrated deep into defended airspace. Therefore the development of power-assisted gun mountings was not encouraged.

The designers at Bristol Aircraft developed a power-operated dorsal gun turret for the wireless operator/air gunner in the Blenheim. This was a unique approach to solving the dual problem of protecting the air gunner from the harsh environment of high-speed flight and of relieving him of the considerable manual effort needed to move a machine gun against a combination of air and G loads. The Bristol turret designed by L.G. Frise was of particular interest because the gun could be trained independently of the turret's rotation, thereby enabling the gun to be aligned tangential to the turret's circumference as with the earlier 'flexible' gun mountings, such as the Scarff. When the Frise turret was being designed and developed the optical reflector sight had not superseded the ring and bead type. Therefore a fundamental feature of the design was the method by which the gunner's head was kept in alignment with the gun as it was elevated. A system of hydraulic jacks raised or lowered the gunner's seat in step with the elevation of the gun. Unlike other powered gun mountings, the Bristol turret was trained by a hydraulic jack rather than a rotary hydraulic motor. To reduce drag when not in use the cupola of the Blenheim's turret could be retracted. However, the Frise turret was an awkward location for the radio equipment because it had to share space with the pillars, jacks, lever arms and other mechanisms of the turret. The operator had to reach round the central pillar in order to adjust the controls, including changing coils, of the type 1082/1083 radio sets.

Although the Blenheim Mk I had two engines there was only one electric generator and one hydraulic pump; both were driven by the port engine. Should the port engine fail electric and hydraulic power were lost. The gun turret was deprived of power whenever the pilot selected either the operation of the flaps or the undercarriage. This was not an ideal arrangement because for one thing it made the aircraft very vulnerable to attack during take-off and landing.

The Frise turret was designed to fit into the narrow fuselage of the Blenheim. In contrast the turrets designed by Frazer Nash (FN) of Nash & Thomson were initially designed for tail and nose mountings in the new generation of 1930s bombers for the RAF. They were true turrets in that the gunner, his seat, sight, controls and the

guns and their ammunition tanks revolved as an integral unit. Frazer Nash had developed a powered gun mounting for the back cockpit of the Hawker Demon, to shelter and relieve the gunner of some of the effort in traversing a gun against the blast of the slipstream. At the time it was a step toward improving the lot of air gunners. As previously mentioned, the first mark of the Wellington had completely enclosed nose and tail gun mountings in which the gunner's seat did not rotate with the guns. They were not satisfactory and were replaced by FN turrets. At the time little thought was given to the possibility that a fighter could attack from the beam and be in the 'dead' arcs of fire. As would happen in WWII, Hampden gunners manning the flexible mounted guns in the upper and lower positions of the Hampden would be unable to traverse fully on

Close up of the mechanism of the FN turret for the Hawker Demon. In this example a camera gun is fitted. The reflector sight is mounted on the back of the camera.
(Reproduced courtesy of DERA)

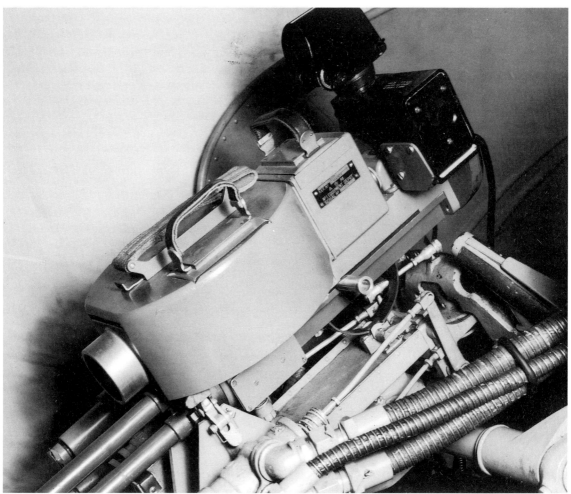

the beam. One formation of Hampdens would be cut down one by one starting with the aircraft at the wing position.

There were many variations among the powered gun mountings and powered turrets in the RAF at the end of the 1930s. Their importance to the subject of this book is the improvement they made to the effectiveness of air gunners and to their comfort.

Defiant

The Defiant designed in 1936 ushered in a new concept for crew positions. It had no fixed forward-firing guns even though it was intended to be a bomber-destroyer. All its offensive armament was concentrated in a four-gun powered turret abaft the pilot's cockpit. It was schemed in advance of a successful radar reporting and fighter control network. It was envisaged that the four-gun turret could be brought to bear on enemy bomber formations. However, this WWI tactic depended on the Defiant being in a favourable position relative to the enemy. That would be difficult to achieve from a standing patrol line unless the line was across the enemy's track and close to his height. The Boulton Paul four-gun turret provided a new experience and place of work for air gunners. No longer the fierce blast of the air stream and the reasonable space of the open cockpit. Now the gunner would be close confined among guns and machinery. The system of power and control adopted by Boulton Paul was a combination of electric and hydraulic power, unlike the competing FN all-hydraulic system. Both systems demanded a power supply from the engines which in the 1930s was not always available. The controls of the FN turrets were of the twist and turn type similar to the throttle control of a motorbike: twist to elevate the guns, turn to traverse the turret. In contrast the Boulton Paul turrets had joystick control which combined elevation and traverse actions.

The pilot's cockpit in the Defiant was typical of its era. It was functional with wheels, levers, knobs, switches and instruments mounted in positions preferred by the production engineers rather than any opinions a pilot might have on the subject. However there was one item which was an improvement over other cockpits. This was the control column mounted on an extension of the adjustable seat structure so that its position relative to the pilot's hands remained constant.

The dive-bomber

The United States Navy (USN) was an enthusiastic advocate of dive-bombing. Its potential was advertised in books and films during the 1930s. The USN encouraged Hollywood to make films about the dive-bomber. A typical sequence would be that of a test pilot having his body tightly bound with tape to prevent a 'blackout' during the high G pull-out at the bottom of a terminal velocity dive. In 1938 the USN introduced special 'G' belts for dive-bomber pilots. The RAF/RN Fleet Air Arm recognised that dive-bombing might provide a cure for the hitherto often inaccurate high-level bombing technique. The *Luftwaffe* at the time was specifying that some of its new multi-engine bombers be capable of making steep dive attacks. However, with hindsight this was a decision that subsequently handicapped German aircraft development and influenced cockpit design, particularly fenestration.

Dive-bombing required some special sighting equipment. To achieve the optimum diving angle for a particular set of conditions the pilot needed a reference line which could be 'held' against the horizon during the dive. This could be as simple as lines painted on the windscreen or as elaborate as the stabilised optical dive-bombing sights developed in Germany.

Take aim

Since the end of WWI there were only two standard types of gunsights used in the RAF, the United States air services and in some other air forces: the Aldis and the ring-and-bead; the latter sometimes had a Norman vane type foresight. However, neither was suitable for modern air fighting. A better form of sight was available. This was the collimated optical reflector sight which did away with the need to align the fore and back sights of a ring and bead sight and which did not restrict the pilot's or gunner's field of view. Patent drawings were published during WWI. In 1918 the details of Sir Howard Grubb's patent of 1900

Barr & Stroud GM2 reflector sight (RAF Mk II) adopted in 1938 as the standard sight for fighter aircraft.
(R. Wallace Clarke)

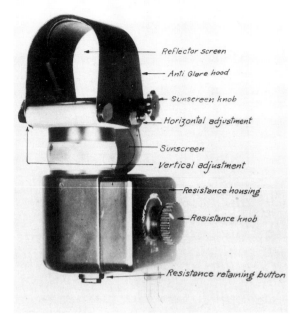

Barr & Stroud optical reflector gunsight for turret and manually aimed guns produced for the RAF in time for WWII.
(R. Wallace Clarke)

for a collimated, i.e. focused at infinity, gun-sight were used by Oigee of Berlin to develop a reflector sight for aircraft use. After WWI Barr & Stroud of Glasgow developed the GD1 reflector sight. This was tested at Martlesham Heath on an Avro 504K. An improved version, the GD2B, followed. Reflector sight development continued throughout the 1920s culminating in the GD5 of 1934, designed specifically for the Hawker Demon fighter. This and other reflector sights used the sloping Triplex glass of the windscreen as the reflecting surface. This arrangement was not satisfactory. Eventually the GM2 reflector sight

with an integral reflector was adopted for the RAF as the Mk II.[2] An initial order for 1,600 was placed on Barr & Stroud and the first units were delivered in 1937. Parallel development in Germany produced the REVI series of collimated reflector sights. In France the Baille-Lemaire was provided for fighters in 1937 and in Italy there was San Giorgio. The first standard fighter reflector sight for the USAAC was the N-1 of 1936. However, Russia was well behind other countries and it was not until 1940 that the first type, the PBP-1, went into production.

Throughout the development years of the reflector sight in Britain it was subjected to high levels of secrecy. Rarely were printed descriptions and illustrations released outside the RAF. Secrecy was helped by the financial restrictions of the 1920s and 30s, resulting in few aircraft equipped with the new sights. The early models had no reflector glass so there was little to be seen above the top of the instrument panel in the cockpit. This helped to conceal the presence of the new method of aiming a fighter's guns.

The first RAF squadron to be equipped with

production standard reflector sights was 65 with its Gladiator fighters. The press was not given access to information on the sight, but the optical principles were well known in gunnery circles. Although the Mk II sight was to be standard on all fighters few were equipped with it until the supply problems were sorted out. At first the Hurricane and Spitfire pilots had to make do with the traditional ring-and-bead sight. No provision appears to have been made to install an Aldis sight as a temporary measure. At this time

The compact Barr & Stroud GJ3 type reflector sight mounted on a camera gun.
(Reproduced courtesy of DERA)

Mk I Spitfire. A shortage of reflector sights in 1938 has meant that a ring-and-bead sight has had to be fitted. The large black lever on the right is for the hand-operated pump for raising and extending the undercarriage and flaps. This required the pilot to change hands on the controls after take-off. Subsequent versions of the Spitfire had a better arrangement.
(Vickers)

American fighters, particularly in the USN, were still being fitted with an Aldis sight mounted externally to the windscreen. In 1926 Barr & Stroud designed a reflector sight for 'free' mounted guns. This went through a number of tests and subsequent improvements until the Mk III (for turret and flexible guns) went into production in 1937, and was used throughout WWII; as was the Mk II (for fixed guns).

The open gunner's cockpit of WWI lingered on into the 1930s and even into the 1940s. Westland Lysander twin Browning 7.7mm mounting in back cockpit.
(R. Wallace Clarke)

Wimperis bomb sight which remained standard RAF bomber equipment until the introduction of the stabilised automatic bomb sights from 1940 on.
(Philip Jarrett)

This important item of cockpit hardware deserves a book on its own. Fortunately for readers who wish to know more about this vital element R. Wallace Clarke has written the definitive book on the subject (see bibliography).

An equipment change that affected the cockpit and which emerged with the advent of wing-mounted guns, was the introduction of pneumatic and electrical firing systems in place of the Bowden cable type. With the Bowden control there was a delay between pressing the firing button and the gun firing.

To see at night and to find at sea

In Britain the technical problems of detecting the approach of enemy aircraft and the methods for directing the defending fighters were being solved one by one. The RAF was relying on the CH radar stations to give sufficient warning and details of attack so that it was not necessary to use standing patrols of fighters. The defence system enabled the controllers to position fighters within three or four miles of enemy formations. From that distance the fighter pilots had a reasonable chance of achieving visual contact.

However, if the enemy chose to attack at night the defending fighters had to be positioned to within 500 to 1,000 feet to ensure visual contact. The development of radar sets small enough to be carried in an aircraft was an urgent need. Once again the Heyford found a place in scientific history as an experimental vehicle. An Anson was also used and on one occasion at least, despite the crude equipment, the crew was able, by following the indications displayed on the small CRT, to 'feel' their way back to Martlesham Heath, through low cloud and in poor visibility. At the time, Sqn Ldr de Haga Haig was developing his Radiaura electronic system for what we now call collision-avoidance.

The Anson experiments proved to be seminal to two main branches of radar development: airborne interception (code name AI) and air-to-surface vessel (code name ASV); both of which were to have important effects on cockpit equipment and design.

In the second half of the 1930s scientists in Britain were concentrating on establishing good communications between ground and air and on developing a system which would continuously track the position of defending fighters. As a consequence Pip Squeak was perfected. This was a system whereby the RT set of a fighter was automatically switched on for fourteen seconds in every minute. During this period the HF/DF stations determined its position. For the remainder of each minute the RT was available for controller-pilot communication. HF/DF and Pip Squeak were key elements in RAF Fighter Command's air defence system of the UK based on radar. The importance of Pip Squeak to the history of the cockpit is that it relieved the pilot of the need to keep reporting his assumed position which in any event might not be very accurate.

The USAAC suffered, as the RAF did at the time, from a limited budget. In 1934 there came an opportunity to prove the skill of the air service pilots. President Roosevelt cancelled the air mail contracts with civil operators and handed the job to the USAAC. An odd collection of fighters and bombers was gathered for the task. Armament and other military equipment was removed and room made for the mail bags. Unfortunately most of the USAAC pilots had little, if any, night and instrument flying experience. Their aircraft had neither landing lights, nor instrument lighting. What instruments were available were usually unable to help a pilot much when he found himself caught out in a storm over rugged country. Five pilots were killed, six injured and eight aircraft destroyed. The pilots were determined to uphold the honour of the USAAC despite inadequate aircraft and poor cockpit equipment.

The air mail venture was the start of a determined effort to improve training and instruments so that operations were no longer at the mercy of visibility and night. Civil aviation was perfecting instrument flying under the pressure of keeping to the schedules. The USAAC pursuit squadrons were still having to operate aircraft whose performance and cockpit equipment needed improvement. However, in one respect long-range heavy bomber technology was advanced when the Boeing B-17s took the air.

Their 'civil' side-by-side cockpit, controls and instruments were an important step forward in cockpit design as a whole.

Design for mistakes

Many incidents and accidents were the result of mishandling the engine controls. If the pilot mishandled the throttle when opening up the engine after a glide the engine might stop. Gliding for too long, thereby letting the engine become cold, was another cause of failure. Spark plugs could oil up unless the pilot remembered to give bursts of throttle at intervals when gliding and when taxying before take-off. A typical example of poor cockpit design leading to disaster occurred when the pilot of an RAF Fairey Battle operated

A tangle of plumbing and wires in a French air force Breguet 693. Note the throttles are fully forward in the closed position. This reverse arrangement applied to most French and Italian military aircraft until after WWII.
(Aeroplane Monthly)

The right-hand side of a Breguet 693 cockpit.
(*Aeroplane Monthly*)

the fuel tank selector controls incorrectly and the engine stopped. He tried to restart it by pulling the throttle back to the 'start' position. But this activated the undercarriage warning horn. To stop the noise, he switched off the horn circuit. Unfortunately it was interconnected with the ignition system and therefore the engine could not be restarted. In another example the pilot of a Hart began to search for landmarks in order to check his position. As he reached for a map he accidentally knocked the ignition switches down to the 'off' position. Before he could re-start the engine the aircraft hit the ground. Somewhere along the line of cockpit equipment and systems design and pilot training, this eventuality had not been foreseen.

In connection with the above events it is noted that in 1938 a prototype Fairey Battle light

bomber was written off after a forced landing. The pilot had moved the fuel tank lever to the right to select the starboard tank. Unfortunately the designer of cockpit equipment had arranged the selector lever to move to the left for the right tank. Apparently from drawing board to assembly of the complete aircraft no one had questioned this example of odd ergonomics. It suggests that, as so often happened, the opinions of a test or experienced pilot were not sought at any stage of the design process. Fuel system mishandling was a significant contributor to the loss of aircraft. The ground crew might fail to fill the fuel tanks properly and the pilot then fail to check the fuel contents before taking off. In the 1930s, fuel tank contents indicators were either rudimentary and difficult to read or inaccurate and unreliable.

An analysis of causes of accidents in the RAF during six months of flying in the 1930s suggested that 25% of the engine failure cases were due to pilot error. Sixty-seven accidents and incidents were attributed to pilot error. However, the report did not identify those 'pilot error' accidents in which poor cockpit design was a contributory cause.

In the UK efficient cockpit design was often inhibited by the reluctance on the part of aircraft manufacturers to depart from their established standards. Therefore what had sufficed for the previous type would have to do for the next: that is provided it met the Air Ministry specification. The 30 or so private aircraft companies were often short of money, particularly the smaller ones, and could not afford to indulge in research into better cockpit equipment and arrangements. With few

exceptions the British aircraft industry was unable to take advantage of, or chose to ignore, the benefits of standardisation of cockpit equipment in position, type and function.

Instrument flight

'Only owls and fools fly at night' used to be a common expression among aviators. It fell into disuse as more and better 'blind flying' instruments and techniques became available. In 1937 the British Air Ministry stated: 'Instruments in the future will be grouped together'. The RAF took a significant step forward, compared with other air forces, when it adopted a standard arrangement of the principal flight instruments. This became the RAF's Basic Six panel consisting of airspeed indicator top left, artificial horizon at top centre, vertical speed top right and along the bottom row from the left the altimeter, the directional gyro

Gloster Gladiator biplane fighter. This is the 'Sea' version but is virtually standard with all Gladiators c. 1939. Notice the open 'bilges'. Aperiodic compass between the pilot's feet and an RAF Basic Six instrument panel.
(Shuttleworth)

Bristol Blenheim Mk I (short nose). It appears neat and tidy but in practice many of the controls were difficult to reach and operate.
(British Aerospace)

heading indicator and the turn and bank indicator. Because aircraft in those days often had poor rates of climb the indicator was called the rate of climb instrument. Going 'downhill' was not conducted with the same precision as would be required in later years. It was also the progenitor of the post-war vertical speed indicator.

The Basic Six panel was a logical arrangement compared with the seemingly muddled arrangement of instruments used by other air forces. In America the arrangement of the principal instruments was related to the 'needle, ball and airspeed' method of basic training. The Basic Six arrangement was in marked contrast to the instrument panel of the American Grumman Avenger TBF, for example, in which the principal flight and engine instruments were arranged in no apparent order. The flight instruments shared a common panel with the engine indicators so that, for example, boost and rpm were in the same row as airspeed, turn and slip and vertical speed.

An important instrument common to all RAF cockpits was the pilot's magnetic compass. The type P4, for example, was usually mounted in front of the pilot's knees or to one side of the cockpit. It was the primary navigational instrument. The compass had a rotating grid ring graduated over 360 degrees with north marked by

a red arrow. When the pilot needed to alter the aircraft's course onto a new heading he rotated the grid ring until the required course was set against the lubber line that represented the fore and aft axis of the aircraft. The aircraft was then turned until the grid wires were lined up with the magnetic needle and with the red arrow set against the northern crosswire of the needle. The operation was simple but there was always the danger that the pilot might inadvertently align the black, south, arrow against the needle. If that happened a reciprocal course would be flown. The use of the magnetic compass is described in some detail because it is a good example of an instrument that required some manipulation on the part of the user before it provided the required answer. Today we expect an instrument to display information unambiguously and not be capable of inducing errors on the part of the user. In contrast to the large aperiodic compass of RAF aircraft, were the distant-reading, gyro-based, magnetic compass systems installed in German and American military aircraft. These required only a moderate-sized unit on the instrument

One of the most distinguishing features of RAF cockpits prior to about 1945: the P Type aperiodic magnetic compass used in conjunction with the Sperry Directional Gyro Indicator.
(Sperry Gyroscope Co.)

panel. Eventually similar systems were fitted to RAF aircraft from about 1941 onward.

Night experience

The undoubted improvements in instrumentation were not being used to the advantage of RAF Bomber Command pilots. In 1937 only 84 had their log-books endorsed as qualified for night flying. The annual flying hours for the command were about 130,000 day and only 8,700 night. In two years' flying the command's pilots made 478 forced landings after failing to work out their size down positions.[3] Following his tour of inspection of squadrons, Sir Edgar Ludlow-Hewitt, C-in-C Bomber Command reached the conclusion that 'the command was entirely unprepared for war and unable to operate except in fair weather'.[4] In retrospect, it is obvious that the weak condition of Bomber Command arose from the limitations on flying hours, insufficient training and lack of suitable equipment; especially for night flying.

As late as 1939 the RAF differentiated between those who were permitted to fly in cloud and those who were not. A Blenheim pilot lost control in thick cloud at night and the aircraft crashed. The squadron standing orders prohibited flight above cloud in a Blenheim for all but the most experienced pilots. From the proceedings of the Court Martial of the pilot came the caveat that 'Until modifications have been made, the Blenheim is not considered suitable for casual cloud flying.' The pilot's experience in a Blenheim was limited to eleven hours of which only two and half hours were solo. One unanswered question is: to what extent did the unsatisfactory arrangement of the controls and instruments contribute to the accident?

Bristol Blenheim IV (long nose). Compared with the Mk I the navigator has a proper chart table under the 'scalloped' part of the aircraft nose.
(British Aerospace)

Simulation

From the earliest years of powered, heavier-than-air flight devices have been used to simulate or replicate the controls and instruments. Simulators have been as simple as a chair mounted on a frame with a control column and rudder bar used to teach the basic co-ordinated control movements.

In 1919 the Anderson device measured a pilot's skill at co-ordinating control about axis. Reid and Burton developed a flight simulator with controls and instruments used to assess a potential pilot's control ability and suitability for flying bombers or fighters.[5] In 1929 Edward Link developed his Trainer. This was a replica fuselage and cockpit with controls and instruments which responded to movements of the controls. The Link Trainer could pitch, yaw and bank. With the hood closed a pupil could learn to fly on instruments and to practise navigational procedures such as intercepting a radio beam and making an approach to an airfield. The instructor had a control desk on which a 'crab' moved across a chart and inked the track of the simulated aircraft. The Link Trainer became an essential part of a pilot's progress. It reduced training costs because it cost less per 'flying' hour than a real aircraft and was unaffected by the weather.

Link's first simulator went through a number of improvements. It was used by air forces in both the USA and Britain as a key training aid. In 1941 Link developed, in association with the Weems, a celestial navigation trainer. This was used by the USAAC and the RAF not only for celestial navigation training but as a crew procedures trainer.

Ab initio

In the 1930s there were few enclosed cockpit type aircraft for *ab initio* training. The Tiger Moth and the Magister used by the RAF for *ab initio* training had open cockpits. The former of 1932 was a modified version of the successful de Havilland Gipsy Moth. The principal changes related to the cockpit being the inverted engine to improve the forward view, the cabane structure further forward and the wings swept back to allow easier exit from the front, instructor's cockpit when wearing a parachute. The Magister

was the final development of the 1935 Miles Hawk Major. Like the Tiger Moth, it had to have a number of modifications to its civil-school original. For example, the cockpits had to be enlarged to make room for seat-type parachutes.

The majority of primary trainers had tandem seating; although the Blackburn B2 was a side-by-side biplane trainer. There was much debate then and subsequently over the merits of the instructor being alongside the pupil and not in another cockpit. Both the American air forces and the German *Luftwaffe* tended to use tandem-seat biplane trainers for *ab initio* instruction.

Advanced training cockpits

Many air forces in the 1930s provided only two types of aircraft for pilot training. A simple low-powered monoplane or biplane and a trainer version of a first-line aircraft. This arrangement sufficed when the difference between the performance of the two types was not too great. However, once air forces started to include aircraft with a comparatively high landing speed and wing loading the need for an intermediate or advanced trainer was highlighted. The step from

The Link Trainer, developed in 1929, could roll, pitch and yaw. It was a major contributor to instrument flight training. (Link)

an ab initio type to, say, the He 111 and Blenheim or Bf 109 and Hurricane was too great and therefore there had to be an intermediate stage of training with suitable aircraft.

In the RAF pilots often had to convert from single-engine *ab initio* aircraft to twin-engine types 'in squadron'. For example in one squadron in 1937 converting to twin-engine Blenheims, the pilots had to use the Anson in order to obtain the twin-engine endorsement stamp in their log-books. They were not all that impressed with the Anson as a step towards flying the Blenheim because the two aircraft had little in common.

Avro Anson trainer and ocean reconnaissance aircraft with the typical pilot-on-left with gangway to the right layout used for the majority of RAF multi-engine aircraft from 1930 onward. (Flight Intl)

The former had a flat approach to land, whereas the latter had a steeper approach with a tendency to undershoot rather than overshoot, as with the Anson. The Anson had fixed-pitch propellers and a manually operated undercarriage in contrast to the variable pitch propellers and power-operated undercarriage of the Blenheim. The Anson was also more forgiving of mistakes and therefore did not prepare a pilot adequately for the sometimes lethal characteristics of the new multi-engine types about to enter service. To meet the bomber-trainer and the fighter-trainer roles new special-ised types were ordered such as the Airspeed Oxford, Miles Master and the North American Harvard.

Cockpit design in general in this period made no concessions to standardisation among *ab initio* and intermediate trainers and first-line aircraft.

HP Hampden. *The high-set position of the Basic Six instrument panel and the wheel relative to the lower edge of the windscreen emphasises the good view afforded the pilot. Note the crude mechanical interlock between the ignition switches and the undercarriage control (left middle).*
(*Aeroplane Monthly*)

Little attempt was made to accustom pupil pilots to a standard set of controls and instrument layout applicable to all the aircraft types so that when they progressed from the *ab initio* cockpit to the next stage it was into a similar cockpit; albeit with more instruments and controls. In other words, the cockpit of a Bücker Jungmeister or a Tiger Moth should have been, respectively, a simplified version of that in the Bf 109 or Spitfire. As it was, the equipment in the cockpit of a Tiger Moth bore no resemblance, other than in basic details, to that in the Miles Master: in the same way the latter's cockpit was significantly different from that of the Spitfire.

Airspeed Oxford

In many respects the RAF's Oxford, particularly the cockpit, was in advance of the twin-engine training aircraft of other air forces; albeit there were few foreign types with which to make a comparison. A retractable undercarriage, flaps and a well equipped cockpit were features intended to give trainee pilots a sound introduction to the problems and tasks to be faced when flying first-line twins. Although the Oxford's Cheetah engines had fixed-pitch propellers, nevertheless the design office provided a dummy propeller pitch control. This enabled a pupil pilot to become familiar with the more extensive cockpit drill for first-line aircraft based on a mnemonic, such as 'HTMPFFG' for Harness, Trim or Throttle friction, Mixture, Pitch, Fuel, Flaps, Gyro or Gills.

Reference to the cockpit of the Oxford serves to emphasise the previous comments about the lack of standardisation among British aircraft types in the 1930s. The engine controls were to the pupil pilot's right-hand: but when he graduated to a Blenheim or Wellington the engine controls were to his left hand; if to a Whitley or to an American Hudson they were to the right.

Miles Master

The Master was derived from the Kestrel Trainer. This was a graceful, sleek aircraft powered by a Rolls-Royce Kestrel engine. The handling

Miles Master I advanced RAF trainer. A more complex cockpit than that of the Tiger Moth or Magister. The tube at the top of the photograph is part of the WWI Gosport 'intercom' between the pupil and the instructor in the back cockpit; and there was no radio. (Aeroplane Monthly)

characteristics, as intended, were similar to those of both the Hurricane and the Spitfire. A number of major changes had to be made to the original design before a production order was given. The windscreen, cabin top and fuselage aft of the cockpits were modified. These changes were in order to match the aircraft to its role with RAF Service Flying Training Schools. Because the design of the Master started after that of the Hurricane and the Spitfire the cockpit was more advanced in detail and layout. For example the engine, flap and undercarriage levers were concentrated in one location close to the pilot's left hand. A constant-speed propeller was fitted even though a pupil pilot might, on reaching a more advanced stage of training, have to revert to the fixed-pitch propellers still being fitted to some

Hurricanes and Spitfires.

The canopy of the Master I provided excellent arcs of view for the pupil pilot in the front seat. The instructor seated aft could raise his seat to see forward during take-off and landing. The top part of the canopy above the instructor hinged upward to provide a windscreen. The complete canopy was hinged on the starboard side for access to both seats. After a number of aircraft had been lost when the canopy inadvertently flew open, broke off and struck the empennage, a more conventional two-part sliding canopy was introduced. Although the Master cockpit was generally to an advanced standard when compared with the cockpits of other aircraft, in two particulars it was out-of-date. There was no inter-communication equipment other than a WWI Gosport tube and there was no RT. In 1939 the RAF did not as a rule equip its *ab initio* and advanced trainer aircraft either with an intercom or RT. An RAF pupil pilot flying solo was more than on his own. Once away from the airfield circuit during night flying and over sparsely populated regions and with no radio it was very easy to become lost. This handicap may have contributed to the number of pupil pilots who crashed after attempting to find their way to an airfield at night or in poor visibility.

Notes

1. King, H.F. (1971) *Armament of British Aircraft*, Putnam.
   Wallace Clarke, R. (1994) *British Aircraft Armament*, Patrick Stephens.
2. Wallace Clarke. op cit. p. 135 et seq.
3. Terrain, J. (1985) *The Right of the Line*, p. 84. Hodder & Stoughton.
4. Ludlow-Hewitt, Air Marshal Sir John, Letter to Air Ministry. AHB Box 2 Folder 7.
5. Rolfe, Dr J.M. (1973) *Applied Ergonomics* 4, 2., pp 84–90.

CHAPTER FOUR

1939 – 1944

The WWII cockpit figuratively stands at one of the more significant milestones in aviation history because it marks the decline of WWI ideas and equipment. The three air forces, British, French and German, that joined battle over northern France at the end of 1939 exhibited marked differences in cockpit equipment.

Most of the equipment and operational practices, both within and without the cockpit, at the beginning of WWII would not have been strange or unfamiliar to a WWI pilot or crewman. Admittedly the number of instruments had increased significantly and most still presented their information in the shape of pointers moving over numeric scales. There was also a greater number of switches for electrical circuits. Nevertheless, in general and with the notable exception of radar, the technology of the cockpit of WWII was essentially similar to that of the earlier war. In the USA and in the UK in particular cockpit design had progressed by a series of evolutionary steps as improved technologies became available during the 1920s and 1930s. Each new generation of pilots, a generation being about five years, learnt to fly on aircraft whose design reflected the standards of ten or twenty years earlier. They then progressed to monoplane aircraft whose performance and abilities demanded enclosed cockpits, retractable undercarriages, flaps, supercharged engines and variable-pitch propellers and, most importantly, instruments that permitted flight through cloud and on a moonless night.

In contrast to the evolutionary progress of the cockpit in America and Britain, the cockpits of German aircraft, particularly for multi-engine types, reflected the 'clean sheet of paper' advantage of the *Luftwaffe*. After 1918 multi-engine aircraft technology in Germany was mostly confined to civil transport aircraft development. The need to mount an engine in the nose of the fuselage, because the total power of two engines was insufficient, compromised the cockpit shape and bomb-aiming position of the tri-motor aircraft. In the 1930s the emergence of engines of 800 bhp or higher provided the opportunity to design twin-engine bombers whose fuselage nose was shaped to accommodate pilot, navigator and bomb-aimer close to each other and to provide wide arcs of view.

The information and control interface

Two aspects of the WWII cockpit need to be noted when describing equipment and the tasks of aircrew. First: some instruments had to be interpreted in order to obtain the required information. This included applying correcting factors in order to obtain a 'true' reading. Secondly, engine control and monitoring was often without the benefit of automatic systems. For example American engines were not, in general, equipped with automatic boost and mixture controls which meant that the pilot had to watch the engine instruments carefully when making large throttle movements. In contrast British and German engines were given more comprehensive automatic controls. These relieved the pilot of the need to monitor engine indications constantly, particularly when concentrating on a target or during an aerial battle. For example, later versions of the Spitfire even had the propeller pitch control linked to the throttle.

Today we are used to the concept of the man-machine interface and to integrated systems throughout an aircraft. We now expect that some systems will have built-in intelligence so that they can perform their functions without frequent human intervention. They are also expected to have built-in test (BIT) and self-monitoring: features in 1939 which were virtually unknown within the present meaning of those terms.

A persistent feature of cockpit design in general, particularly in America, Britain and

France, was the lack of standardisation of the principal components. Important items might be on the left in one type of aircraft and on the right in another: some might be in front of the pilot, others behind his elbow. (Today, aviation English, under the influence of America, uses the word 'commonality' having forgotten the meaning of the word 'standardisation'.)

Occasionally there would be an article in the aviation technical press arguing for the maximum standardisation of the type and position of controls and instruments. Given time and no distracting events, such as sudden engine failure, a

The cockpit of a Spitfire c. 1940. Points of interest are: the two-position rudder pedals; the typical P4 aperiodic compass between the pilot's feet; the RAF Basic Six arrangement of the flight instruments and the knurled ring on the cross tube for mounting the reflector sight.
(Vickers)

pilot in an unfamiliar cockpit may be able to make the correct control selections. There are numerous anecdotes of the type: 'There I was upside down, pointers swinging across their dials, trying to find the flap lever'. The extent to which variations among different aircraft types contributed to errors on the part of pilots is not recorded.

A very experienced RAF bomber pilot wrote a most apposite and revealing comment on British cockpit design of the late 1930s, when comparing the Lancaster with the Halifax:

'The variations in cockpit layout were more obvious [differences], and few, in my opinion, [if] any kind of improvement. The [Halifax] throttle-levers, for example, came far less easily to hand – although I liked the friction lever better, and the trim tab controls, in contrast with the compact unit of the Lancaster, were all over the place. The undercarriage and flap levers, on the other hand, were much too close together; fumbling for them in the dark, down beside your right thigh, you could be forgiven for mistaking one for the other, and that might make a late overshoot more exciting than need be. The lever for the bomb-doors was right there with them, but it did not function in the natural sense, as they did, up for up and down for down, and although a tangle over that would not matter on a Lincolnshire bombing range, I imagine it could be an embarrassment over, say, the Wilhemstrasse. The blind-flying instruments – airspeed indicator, altimeter, gyro compass, turn-and – slip indicator – were in their usual position on the panel in front of you (even Handley Page accepted the standard pattern there) but the other forty-odd dials and gauges were spread around the cabin as though somebody had thrown them in through the window and fitted them wherever they hit.'[1]

German cockpits had equipment, including instruments which made them instantly distinguishable from those of other air forces. In general they were equipped, both in detail and overall, to a very high standard compared with those of British aircraft. Switches, selector levers, instruments and the minutiae, such as labels, were carefully designed. Cockpit equipment reflected the generally high quality of German design and manufacture. American multi-engine aircraft cockpits, compared with British, were in general far more comfortable for the crew. In some aircraft there was extensive padded lining to isolate the crew from external noise. Ash trays were often provided. French cockpits prior to 1940 were different from both German and British. One distinguishing feature being the 'reverse' throttle action.

It is no exaggeration to record that if, in the 1940s, you were guided blindfolded into an unknown aircraft cockpit your nose would easily determine whether you were in a German, British or American aircraft. There were readily discernible national aircraft smells.

Fenestration

In the 1930s and 1940s cockpit fenestration design for multi-engine aircraft could be divided into two basic profiles: the traditional stepped nose, as common in civil transports, and the unbroken

nose line favoured for many German aircraft; and later in the war adopted by Boeing for the B-29. This was the first large pressurised, high-altitude, long-range (5,000 miles) bomber. The B-29 cockpit, or rather the flight deck, because it was flat decked and spacious, was inside the continuously curved nose section and without a stepped windscreen. Although the semi-spherical array of small windows was intended to give wide fields of view forward, upward, below and on both bows it exposed the crew to intense sunlight. Extending

B-29. The two sets of pilots' controls and instruments are separated by a gangway to the forward bomb-aiming position. In this photograph the aircraft commander has his right hand on the wheel brakes control levers. The engine controls are out of sight alongside his left arm. The instrument panel includes double pointer indicators for manifold pressure (boost) and rpm, each instrument serving two engines.
(Boeing)

There were numerous frames in the cockpit transparencies of a Bf 109; even in this late -G version.
(Peter Ottery)

the sun blinds obviously defeated the designer's original object of providing maximum arcs of view. At night, particularly in rain, the multiple reflections of lights on the ground, such as when landing, gave the pilot a dangerously distorted view. Eventually some improvement was gained by using flat panels, in place of the originally curved panels, for those in front of the pilots. Because of the width of the flight deck and the need for a gangway forward to the bomb-aimer's station in the extreme nose, there was no central control pedestal as in the B-17 and B-24 for example. Each of the two pilots had a control pedestal at his outboard hand. The throttles on these pedestals for the four engines were the typical Boeing 'bar' type, as used in the B-17.

Perhaps one of the most significant changes in cockpit fenestration that occurred at the end of the 1930s concerned the design of canopies on single-seat aircraft. Pilots of biplane fighters disliked a completely enclosed cockpit because it added to the difficulties of visually searching for the enemy. The pilot's view upward, downward

and to the sides was already well wooded by the wings, the interplane struts and rigging wires.

Each of the three principal fighters in the Battle of Britain in 1940 had a distinctive cockpit windscreen and canopy. The Spitfire started life with a windscreen and canopy that eventually proved unsuitable for air combat. The curved panels distorted the pilot's view and he could not turn his head sufficiently to see astern. The demands of air fighting prompted major changes to the shape of the cockpit canopy. Some Spitfire pilots found great difficulty in sliding back the canopy when attempting to bale-out. Martin-Baker devised a modification whereby a series of plungers freed the canopy from its runners. To free the canopy the pilot pulled on a small red ball which hung just above his forehead. In contrast to the Spitfire, the Hurricane's canopy was made up of many small flat panels. Unlike the Spitfire, that eventually acquired a bubble canopy, the Hurricane retained its original canopy profile and structure to the end of its active life.

The Bf 109 canopy and windscreen had an angular shape made up of individual flat panels. The canopy was hinged on the right to allow access to the cockpit. The cockpit closely confined the pilot: its dimensions seemed to have been related to the average shoulder width and seated height of pilots and therefore made no allowance for the large or tall pilot. Colonel Charles Lindbergh flew a Bf 109 during one of his visits to Germany before the war when he was gathering facts for his writings on the wonders of National Socialism and the overwhelming might of the *Luftwaffe*. Although he was 6′ 4″ tall he does not seem to have commented adversely on the cramped cockpit: or was he avoiding upsetting his hosts?

Many new aircraft types which entered service in the early 1940s, such as the P-47, Mustang and Typhoon, did not provide a good view astern. In contrast, from the start the FW 190 and the Westland Whirlwind had a cockpit canopy profile giving wide arcs of view including the important 'over the shoulder' view. Taxying the long-nosed fighters of the 1940s required frequent changes of

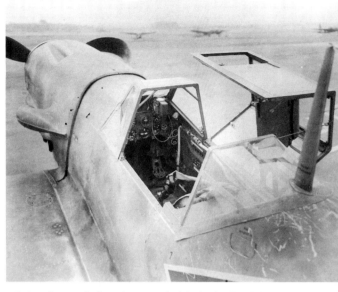

Bf 109F showing the hinged canopy which had to be closed when taxying. A section of the armour plating for the pilot's seat was fixed to the canopy.
(P. Jarrett)

Westland Whirlwind with a comparatively tidy cockpit. The thin windscreen frame and the one-piece blown plastic 'bubble' canopy afforded the pilot a good all-round view.
(Derek James)

direction in order to see ahead. In the Bf 109 this problem was aggravated by the need to keep the canopy closed.

The nose and cockpit transparencies of the B-26 Martin Marauder twin-engine bomber are good examples of the advances made under the pressure of war in the development of large areas of double curvature glass and plastic panels.

American cockpits

American air force single-seat cockpits were, in general, larger than those used by other air forces. The control column was set further forward and was higher than those of British and German types. The greater use of electrical systems, as in bombers, meant more switches rather than levers. As mentioned, instrument panel layouts were to no particular standard.

Although the P-39 Bell Airacobra, with its engine behind the pilot, was a late 1930s monoplane design it perpetuated the arrangement of many biplanes in which the fuselage-mounted guns projected into the cockpit. The backs of the two 13mm guns protruded out of the instrument panel and included two large hand grips for manually cocking (arming). The drive shaft forward to the propeller passed under the pilot's seat and between his legs so that the control column had to be forked at the bottom. The Airacobra had a car-type door to the cockpit. A similar arrangement was fitted to the early mark of the British Typhoon: the door, as with side-hinged canopies, had to be closed when taxiing.

Japanese cockpits

Before 1941 the Western nations not only assumed that Japanese pilots were short-sighted but their aircraft were of poor quality. By the end of 1941 Allied pilots realised that the Mitsubishi A6M Zero, for example, was not only an excellent fighter but it was also well equipped and had instruments whose quality matched those of other air forces. In one respect, of course, Japanese pilots were, on average, smaller than their Western counterparts and therefore not so demanding on cockpit space. Incidentally, the Zero's twin 7.7mm fuselage-mounted guns projected back into the cockpit and took up valuable instrument panel space: so much so that the prime panel position in some versions of the A6M immediately under the reflector sight had room only for an artificial horizon and a turn and bank (slip) indicator.

Pilot's position

During WWII there were few departures from the accepted position for the pilot or pilots. This was close to the nose in multi-engine aircraft and behind the engine in single and tandem seat aircraft. Other crew positions could either be concentrated close to the pilot, as in many German aircraft, or dispersed in remotely located gun, bomb-aiming and navigation positions. German design philosophy believed in the morale boosting effect of positioning the crew members close together, as in the Dornier 217 and Junkers 88 and their subsequent variants. The majority of German multi-engine types had only one complete set of pilot's controls and this was to the left of the centre line. A basic set of flight controls might be provided for a seating position on the right.

British medium and large bombers usually only had one pilot's place. This was on the left in order to leave room for a gangway on the right leading to the navigator/bomb-aimer's position in the nose. Examples were the Blenheim, Wellington, Whitley and Hudson. Although the last type was a Lockheed design the crew positions were arranged to meet the RAF's specification. British aircraft with 'two-pilot' cockpits included the Stirling and the Sunderland.

An example of a unique attempt to be different was the B&V 141B. This was an asymmetric single-engine monoplane with the crew in a nacelle to starboard of the engine. The engine nacelle was extended aft to carry the empennage, the tail plane of which extended to port. This arrangement of crew and engine provided excellent arcs of visions in most directions except to the left. In Dr Vogt's proposed P-170 three-engine high-speed bomber project for B&V the pilot and navigator/bomb-aimer were seated in tandem in the extreme tail.

Single and tandem-seat cockpits world-wide were usually built to a standard arrangement.

Whereas multi-engine cockpits exhibited significant differences among the 'airwar' nations. American multi-engine aircraft cockpits often reflected the civil flight deck arrangement with two pilots sitting side by side and with the pilot on the right responsible for managing the engines and systems. This layout was also used in Japanese bombers. The 'standard', side-by-side, two-pilot cockpit of so many American multi-engine aircraft of WWII was not applied to the Douglas Invader (A-26/B-26). This twin-engine attack/bomber, introduced into the USAAF in 1943, positioned the single set of controls to the left of the gangway to provide access to the navigator/ bomb-aimer station in the extreme nose. The engine controls pedestal was on the centre line. A good point and one which was so often lacking in contemporary British cockpits,

B-29 flight deck. Numerous fenestration panels provide wide arcs of view and serve for both pilots' and bomb aimer's positions. The engine control levers are outboard of each pilot.
(Boeing)

were the 'close-to-hand' fuel cock selectors. In American aircraft these were usually of good size, clearly marked and moving in the logical direction. The Invader pilot also benefited from advances made in the forming of large one-piece cockpit windows: there was only one centre pillar to obstruct the forward view whereas in earlier aircraft types there was a multiplicity of small windows.

Variations

Although a number of stereotype arrangements have been described there were also many exceptions to any apparent rules about cockpit design and equipment. Perhaps one of the greatest variations of design in multi-engine aircraft was to be found among the throttles and other engine control levers. There were examples of throttles to the left and examples to the right of the pilot. In German aircraft the engine controls were more often to be found to the left of the pilot. Some types of British aircraft had them to the left and others on a central controls pedestal as in a civil

airliner. American bombers also exhibited differences. The B-17 and the B-24 had the throttles on a central pedestal whereas, as mentioned, each of the two pilots in a B-29 had a set of engine control levers to his outboard side. (The throttle-like levers close to the centre line of a B-29 flight deck were the brake control levers).

Throttle movement

On the subject of throttle levers it is interesting to note the French and Italian preference for the throttle movement of pull back for increased power. French and Italian pilots were accustomed to this arrangement. The reason for this preference may lie with 'steam' engineering in which the internationally accepted stereotype required a wheel or lever to move or rotate counter-clockwise for opening. This applied to the throttle when mounted on the left side of a cockpit and as seen by the pilot. However it could have fatal consequences when pilots of other nations attempted to fly French and Italian aircraft. It so happened that in 1940 a number of American aircraft, such as DB-7s (Bostons) and Curtiss Hawk 75As, originally intended for the French air force, were acquired for the RAF. An important modification was the reversal of the throttle movement.

P-38 Lightning

In WWII there were not many single-seat, twin-engine aircraft. In the UK there were the Westland Whirlwind and Welkin and the de Havilland Hornet and in Germany the Me 262 as examples. In the USA the nine-ton, 52-foot span, P-38 Lightning was an example of the 'trade-off' game in which available engine power, armament and aerodynamic considerations produced different solutions to the demand for a new fighter. The Lightning's single-seat cockpit was part of a short fuselage set on the wing between the two Allison turbo-supercharged engines, whose nacelles extended aft to carry the empennage. The location of the pilot provided good arcs of view in most directions. A feature of the cockpit was the spectacle type aileron control wheel and not a joystick as used for the majority of fighters. The control column was set to the

right of the pilots with a cross over section to bring the wheel central to the pilot's hands, although later versions may have had a stick in place of a wheel.

In 1944 the USAAF started to use P-38s as bombers. The 'lead' aircraft of a formation of P-38 bombers had an extended nose which provided room for a bomb-aimer. Because space in the glazed nose section was limited only a small bomb-aimer could be carried. All aircraft in a formation of P-38s released their bombs simultaneously on a signal from the 'lead' aircraft.

Open-cockpit aircraft

A number of open-cockpit type aircraft of the 1930s generation were pressed into service in 1939. Among the more interesting was the Fairey Swordfish. This single-engine, three-seat, biplane looked ancient even when, as a prototype, it arrived for assessment at RAF Martlesham Heath in 1934.

The open crew positions of the 'Stringbag', as it was affectionately known in both the Fleet Air Arm (FAA) and the RAF, provided harsh, cramped and uncomfortable conditions for the pilot, observer (navigator) and telegraphist-air gunner (TAG). The crew categories reflected the aircrew practices of the pre-war FAA when, prior to 1938, it was part of the RAF. In those years observers were naval officers, the TAGs were naval ratings and the majority of pilots were RAF embarked for a tour of naval flying. For over water flights away from the carrier and with primitive radio aids to navigation a highly qualified naval navigator, who was also familiar with the characteristics of enemy vessels and the most likely position of their 'mobile airfield', the carrier, was most essential.

The pilot's cockpit, below the cut out in the trailing edge of the upper wing centre section, was typical of its generation: cluttered and with equipment and instruments mounted in locations convenient to the designer but not necessarily to the pilot. The principal instruments, the type and number of which varied among different marks of the aircraft, were not to the RAF Basic Six arrangement.

The primary offensive role of the Swordfish was

that of launching a torpedo at a height of 100 feet or less above the water. This required accurate visual judging of height on the part of the pilot who could not rely on the altimeter which might read 100 feet too high or too low. A more sensitive altimeter was introduced later in the war. Mention had been made of the importance of the gunsight, both in size and position, in relation to cockpit design. In the 'Stringbag' the pilot used a special sight when making a torpedo attack. This consisted of two horizontal rows of small lamps mounted on rods attached to the cabane struts. The lamps were spaced at intervals representing five knots of target speed. If the speed of the target vessel was estimated, for example, as ten knots then the pilot steered at 90 degrees to its track keeping the second lamp aligned on the target. This simple but effective torpedo sight solved the 'triangle of velocities' so as to aim the torpedo the appropriate distance ahead of the target.

The observer and TAG were in a long open cockpit immediately behind the pilot. The observer went about his navigational tasks in the confined space at the forward end of the open 'bathtub' of a cockpit. He was also close enough to the pilot to be able to convey instructions by thumping the latter on the appropriate shoulder. The TAG's radio sets and single defensive 7.7mm gun took up the back of the cockpit. In 1941 conditions were made even more cramped for the crew when ASV (air-to-surface vessel radar) was installed in the Swordfish. ASV improved even further the FAA's success rate in sinking Axis ships attempting to supply the German and Italian armies of North Africa. The three-man crews of the Swordfish went to war in their open cockpits flying at low level through intense flak when attacking convoys. Others faced hours of numbing cold when on patrol over the Arctic seas. Many times they hoped that the 100 knot or less cruising speed of their 'Stringbag' would overcome a 60-knot gale, so as to get back to their carrier, which was steaming up wind, before they ran out of fuel.

Instruments

Instrument panels also exhibited national characteristics. A notable example, already men-

tioned, was the RAF's Basic Six 'blind flying' panel. A seemingly haphazard arrangement of the instrument panel was used in some German aircraft. But often this could not be avoided because the characteristic extensive fenestration forward, with views from the pilot's seat downward, upward and to the sides, mitigated against a neat athwartships panel. In the He 111 for example many of the flight instruments were

Bf 109. A narrow cockpit with little headroom. The instrument arrangement is very different from that of a contemporary RAF fighter. On the left of the instrument panel is the ignition selector switch with four positions: Magnetos off, No 1 on, No 2 on, 1 and 2 on. The version illustrated does not have the propeller control lever below the Revi gun sight as in earlier models: pitch being integrated with throttle movement. The canopy is hinged along the right side of the cockpit. (P. Jarrett)

above the pilot's eye level.

The 1940 version of the Bf 109 had a very different arrangement from the RAF Basic Six of the primary flight instruments. From left to right, starting top left, in two rows of three they were: altimeter, magnetic compass, boost gauge, airspeed indicator, turn and slip and rpm indicator. Apparently there was no vertical speed indicator. The ignition switches were arranged in what might be termed the 'German-American' style. In place of the individual switches of British cockpits there was one lever moving in a quadrant. The pilot could select: BOTH OFF, M1, M2 or M1 plus M2: M meaning Magneto. Not to be found in British or American cockpits of that era was the propeller pitch indicator of the Bf 109 which in the earlier versions did not have a constant-speed propeller. One item not found in the RAF but common in German aircraft of the period was the round counters for the guns. The reflector type gun sight in the Bf 109 was usually the REVI type. It was offset slightly to starboard.

This has led writers and film makers to assume that the pilot only used his right eye when aiming. Which is as much a nonsense as writers who describe the pilot pressing one eye against the end of an Aldis sight when aiming. The object of both the Aldis and the reflector sights was to collimate the aiming image so that it appeared to be focused at infinity and usable by both eyes together.

Below the main instrument panel was an auxiliary set of controls and indicators. These included: fuel cock lever, gun armament selector and rounds-used indicator, the gunsight dimmer control, combined fuel and oil pressure gauge,

---

B-24 Liberator four-engine bomber. Flight instruments concentrated in front of captain's position; engine instruments on second pilot's panel. Aileron/elevator wheels are on shafts which extend out of the instrument panel. On the centre panel are the Honeywell autopilot controls and to the left of the four white throttle levers is the control knob for the electronically controlled turbo-superchargers.
(Aeroplane Monthly)

undercarriage position indicator, undercarriage selector lever with emergency selector below, fuel contents indicator, oil temperature gauge. The Messerschmitt drawing office staff positioned controls and instruments to suit their needs rather than those of the pilot.

The two principal American heavy bombers in service before the advent of the B-29, the B-17 and B-24 had their main instrument panels arranged so that the second pilot could monitor the engines and systems. This meant that the captain had few instruments on his part of the panel. The flight instruments in the B-17 were on the centre of the main panel. Being an earlier aircraft, the cockpit of the B-17 had fewer electrical systems switches and controls compared with the B-24. On the controls pedestal between the pilots there were throttle, propeller and mixture control levers for each engine along with a master control unit for all four exhaust-turbine superchargers. A Boeing 'trademark' was the arrangement of the four engine throttle levers. These had horizontal grips so that the pilot could, with one hand, move all four together or select either pairs of engines or individual engines.

Gyro magnetic distant-reading compass

In the first two years of the war there was one particular item of equipment which set British cockpits apart from those of other nations. This was the principal compass display. American and German aircraft had remotely located master compass units with repeater instruments in front of the pilot and navigator. The cockpit of an RAF aircraft in the early years of WWII could be easily identified from the large diameter aperiodic magnetic compass with rotatable grid ring which took up a lot of space. As mentioned, in single-engine aircraft it was usually positioned between the pilot's feet. By the end of 1940 the RAF began to make increasing use of the gyro magnetic distant-reading compass. The unit was mounted in a position where it was least affected by adverse magnetic influences. A repeater indicator of aircraft heading was provided on the pilot's instrument panel and in the navigator's compartment.

Engine instruments in American multi-engine aircraft were usually of the type in which one instrument case housed two mechanisms thereby giving two pointer-on-dial presentations; one for each of two engines. This arrangement economised in space on the instrument panel. The British also had some twin read-out instruments, such as rpm indicators. The American twin-display instruments, for example, when set in a row covering four engines and two different sets of parameters, had to be scanned carefully to make sure that a particular reading applied to the correct engine.

Automatic flight system controls

Autopilots were usually selected and programmed through a control and display unit in the cockpit. Typical of the wartime generation of automatic flight control systems (AFCS) was the Minneapolis-Honeywell C-1 system with its distinctive control and selector unit and with two rows of small lamps to indicate when the pilot could engage the system. In the B-24s the unit was mounted on the left side of the central control pedestal. The C-1 was coupled to the Norden stabilised bomb sight. In contrast British multi-engine aircraft were equipped with the less sophisticated Smiths pneumatic autopilot that had been developed in the early 1930s. An improved version which was coupled to the gyro magnetic compass provided automatic course keeping, a feature which had been incorporated in German autopilots before WWII.

An early example of the modern side-stick controller was to be found on some B-24s. A small control column or joystick was mounted alongside the left leg of the aircraft captain. This enabled him to control directly the aircraft through the autopilot when flying in formation. It was an extension of the system whereby the bomb-aimer exercised control of the aircraft in yaw when approaching a target.

Navigational equipment and positions

The pressures of war advanced the performance of aircraft so that greater ranges were possible. Long-range flying by experienced crews had been a feature of aviation in general in the decade before WWII. The skills and professionalism of the pre-war navigators encouraged the develop-

*Navigator (Observer)/bomb-aimer's position in the nose of a
Hampden.*
(R. Wallace Clarke)

ment of specialised equipment as well as the provision of dedicated positions in aircraft for the
navigator.

Accurate navigation in the 1930s was achieved
by combining information obtained from radio
bearings with astronomical observations and
calculations, such as dead reckoning (i.e. deduced
reckoning). The enclosed cockpit became essential
along with a chart table, drift sight and in the
1940s a transparent observation dome for using a
sextant. The provision of a navigator's cockpit or
cabin varied from air force to air force. In the
USA the development of the long-range bombers
as a strategic weapon, such as the B-17, introduced the concept of a navigator's compartment
in the nose of the aircraft.

Contrary to popular belief, the German air
force was developed in the 1930s as a strategic
weapon. However, space and equipment for long-
range navigation was not a feature of many of the
Luftwaffe's bombers used in WWII. Albeit,
navigation was assisted by radio beams which
intersected a target such as *Knickebein*. In
contrast American and British bombers and
maritime patrol aircraft usually had a dedicated
space for a chart table and equipment for the use
of a navigator. As the war progressed and
electronic aids proliferated a navigator could

exercise his trade without the need for a chart
table. In the DH Mosquito, for example, the
navigator sat shoulder-to-shoulder with the pilot
with the majority of the equipment in front of
him.

Although the USAAC had developed long-
range navigational equipment for use over the
great distances between the islands of America's
empire of Pacific islands the training of sufficient
navigators was not given enough attention until
1941. The RAF in the inter-war years had always
had a corps of pilots who specialised in long-
range navigational techniques and provision was
made in the new bombers of the mid-1930s for a
chart table. However, some of the bomber types,
such as the Blenheim and Hampden had no
proper facilities, such as an astrodome, for using a
sextant. The RAF did not introduce specialised
navigators until the mid-1930s. Hitherto navigation had usually been the responsibility of the
second pilot. It was not until 1940 that there was
a sufficient number of specialised navigators as
opposed to the employment of pilots as
navigators. Incidentally, the WWI RFC/RAF

German bomb sight c. 1940.
(Reproduced courtesy of DERA)

classification of Observer included the skill of navigation along with that of bomb-aiming, photography, radio, gunnery and observation. It was not until 1942 that the RAF started to train navigators as opposed to observers. The new navigators had to complete a far more comprehensive course than that of the observer; including the use of the new electronic navigational systems. The tasks of bomb-aiming and visual observation of navigational features and the target area devolved on a new specialist aircrew member.

A typical navigator's station in a large RAF bomber in the second half of WWII included, in addition to the traditional chart table and 'pencil and paper' navigation equipment, the following:

Distant-reading gyro magnetic compass repeater
Airspeed indicator
Altimeter
Oxygen flow indicator
Air thermometer
Demolition switches for secret electronic equipment
H2S radar for navigation and target location
Gee for precise navigation
Air position indicator
Astrograph 'stars-on-chart' projector for astro navigation
Switch and fuse panel for electronic equipment.

Butt Report

Despite the training of aircrew as observers i.e. navigator/bomb-aimer, Britain's ability to strike at Germany's industrial centres was thwarted by the inability of many RAF aircrew to navigate accurately, particularly at night and in low visibility. By 1941 the Butt Report disclosed a set of statistics which showed that few crews found their target and that of those that did few were able to aim their bombs accurately. The bomber navigator at his chart table was neither trained nor equipped to complete the tasks set the RAF by the War Cabinet. Eventually there were improvements to equipment. These included the electro-mechanical air position indicators (API) and air mileage units developed for RAF Bomber Command. The API was fed with the aircraft's magnetic heading, air temperature, airspeed and other data. The navigator's display unit indicated

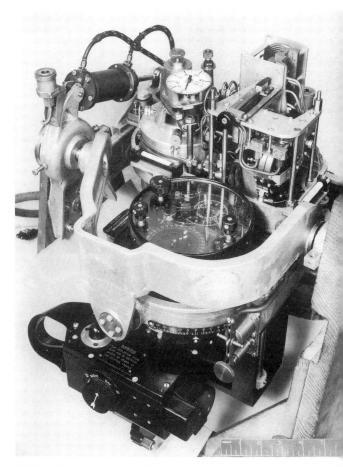

RAF stabilised automatic bomb sight with cover removed to show the gyros and mechanisms which stabilised the bomb-aimer's reflector sight. The sight can be seen bottom left. (Reproduced courtesy of DERA)

the aircraft's position as a numeric readout of the changes in latitude and longitude from the initial or up-dated co-ordinates of position. By the end of 1941 the introduction of Gee and later H2S, (see page 86) and better navigational training methods, began to improve the effectiveness of Bomber Command. These navigational aids are important in the history of the cockpit because they represent a move away from pencil and paper calculations toward instrument systems which when given inputs of information automatically provide an immediate answer.

Radio

In the first year of WWII German single-seat

Marconi general purpose transmitter type T1154 for the RAF. This one was made by E.K. Cole.
(GEC-Marconi)

Marconi general purpose receiver type R1155. The standard receiver, along with the transmitter T1154, for the majority of RAF aircraft from mid-1940 onward.
(GEC-Marconi)

fighters were fitted with an RT set operating in the 2.5 to 3.7 MHz band with a useful range of about 35 miles. The limited range would prove a handicap when Bf 109s were required to escort bombers attacking targets in Britain.

The standard, multi-purpose radio installation in German bombers was the FuG 10 consisting of two receiver units (3–6 MHz and 300–600 kHz) and two transmitter units. In addition there was an intercom unit and a master distant-reading compass used with a DF loop control unit and indicator. These units were usually located in the radio operator's station or cockpit. Because the complete FuG 10 installation was housed in seven or eight standard size modules it could be easily adapted to conform to the available space.

At the start of WWII the RAF's principal airborne radio equipment consisted of the 1082 transmitter and 1083 receiver and the TR 9 RT set. The 1082 and 1083 had plug-in tuning coils. Each coil covered a band of frequencies. Changing to a frequency in another band meant that the operator had to pull out one set of coils and insert another and then re-adjust both transmitter and receiver. To overcome this time

*BAe Hawk 200. Once the weapon-aiming system
sequence and symbology has been selected, using the
up-front control panel at the base of the HUD, the pilot
uses HOTAS (Hands On Throttle and Stick)
operation.*
(British Aerospace)

Joint Primary Air Training System (JPATS) cockpit. Compared with earlier primary trainers the majority of the displays are electronic. In the centre of the panel at the top is the electronic attitude director and below the horizontal situation display. Other features, intended to introduce the pupil pilot to equipment in more advanced performance aircraft, are the black and yellow ejection seat firing handle, the substantial throttle grip and the array of selector buttons on the control column. (Raytheon Aircraft)

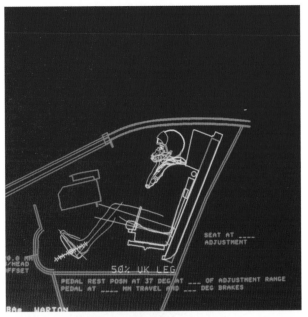

Left: *Computer Aided Design (CAD) showing profile of pilot in relation to seat, canopy, electronic displays and rudder pedals in a single-seat fighter.*
(British Aerospace)

Below: *The realism of modern fighter simulators is very apparent from this shot of the cockpits of an F-15 'engaging' two one-time Soviet fighters.*
(McDonnell Douglas)

Left: A modern multi-function colour display unit. In the mode selected the pilot is able to see the view ahead, as generated by the Forward Looking Infra-Red (FLIR) system, even on a dark night. The numerals show that the aircraft is at 3,072 feet and flying at 275 knots indicated. The peripheral 'soft' keys are used to select other sets of information, such as navigation. (Smiths Industries)

Below: Saab JAS39 Gripen. By the 1980s the increasing reliability and versatility of electronic displays relegated electro-mechanical instruments to a standby role. The Gripen cockpit provides the pilot with 150 sq in of active multi-function colour electronic display area. (Saab AB)

consuming and sometimes difficult operation the 1082 and 1083 were replaced by the Marconi general purpose (GP) 'Jeep' sets (1185–1186). These were put into full scale production in 1940. The advantage of the new sets over the old were the all-wave receiver and the 'push-button' tuned transmitter. A number of different transmitter frequencies could be pre-tuned and then selected by turning large, knurled, coloured knobs to a pre-selected 'clock' position.

Readers may find it incredible that in the RAF in the 1940s RT communication between fighters and bombers was not usually available. A prime example is the ferrying of single-engine fighters from Takoradi on the Gold Coast to Cairo across 3,500 miles of the heart of Africa. A ferry pilot, in the event of trouble, had no RT contact with the 'convoy' leader flying the medium bomber at the head of the formation.

The limited production capacity of the radio industry in the UK was one reason why pupil pilots in the RAF, even at the more advanced stage of their tuition, were without the benefit of RT. A pupil pilot caught out by a sudden deterioration in visibility was very much on his own. The men and women of the ATA who ferried aircraft for the RAF more often than not flew without any form of radio communication with the ground.

Leading the target

A feature common to all aircraft aiming sights since WWI is the provision of rings, beads and symbols to enable the pilot or air gunner to 'lead' the target. If a target is flying directly towards or away from you then the only aiming correction needed is an allowance for 'drop': that is the increasing amount by which a bullet or shell is affected by gravity the farther it travels. When the target is also moving across the line-of-sight allowance also has to be made for this by 'aiming off' or 'leading' the target. In WWI a typical ring-and-bead sight had the ring dimensioned to correspond with a target having a relative crossing speed of 50 mph.

The successful fighter pilots, the Aces, were usually those who had mastered the art of correctly leading the target and using the pattern formed by the tracer bullets. To some extent luck

played its part: in the mêlée of a dogfight over the Western Front enemy aircraft suddenly appeared in the sight and just as quickly disappeared as both aircraft twisted and turned. In other words the situation was far removed from that of the aiming and tracer diagrams in books or on the blackboard in a classroom. Adding to the aiming problem both in WWI and WWII was the limited amount of ammunition that could be carried. In the 'Hollywood' air wars pilots are seen blazing away unaware that in the real world a 20-second burst of fire could use up all the ammunition and might also ruin the gun barrels. Therefore the scientists set about devising a simple 'spot on' method of aiming.

At the beginning of WWII British scientists were developing lead-computing gyro-gunsights. They went into production for Allied aircraft from 1942 onward. The gyro sights were very much larger than the non-gyro reflector sights and therefore filled much of the space behind the windscreen. In contrast German aircraft retained the simpler, non lead-computing, REVI type reflector sights until the end of the war.

Gyro gun sight (GGS) Mk II. The operating system included a mirror fixed on a gyroscope which deflected the aiming symbols so that movement of the target across the line of sight was automatically allowed for. With the GGS the pilot only had to hold the target within the circle of six small diamonds and did not have to offset the target, as with the standard reflector sight. (R. Wallace Clarke)

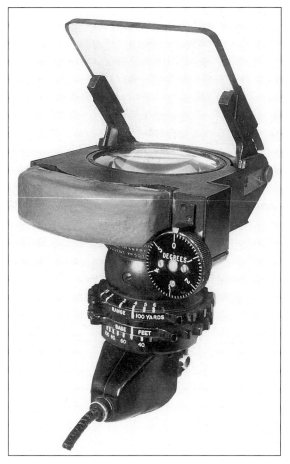

Mk IIL reflector sight in which the optical system could be adjusted to allow for the difference between the trajectories of guns and rockets.
(R. Wallace Clarke)

In addition to obscuring the view forward, the gyro sight started a new trend in throttle design. Hitherto the throttle had been just a simple lever: sometimes with an intercom button and a switch for water-methanol injection selection. The gyro sight required a range input and this was through a twist grip on the throttle lever. This was used by the operator to open or close up the ranging 'pips' displayed in the sight so as to bracket the target. The range information and the previously set wing span of the target were fed to the sight's mechanism as part of the lead-computing function. The introduction of air-launched rockets, when the trajectory was far from flat, required modification of the sights to allow for rocket

'drop'. They also posed a problem in single-engine aircraft because the engine sometimes obscured the target during the attack dive.

At the time of the Allied invasion of Europe in June 1944 the Hawker Tempest V was given a new design of windscreen and improved gyro gunsight. Offensive low-level operations by Spitfires and Typhoon Is had highlighted the limitations imposed on the effectiveness of the pilot/aircraft weapon system. The small windscreen panels and heavy frames along with the reflector glass and brackets of the GM2 sight restricted the forward view. In low visibility conditions there was also a significant loss of light through the reflector glass of the sight as well as a loss of contrast between the aiming graticule image and the view ahead. Modifications at squadron level included eliminating the reflector glass and all but the aiming spot and reflecting the latter directly off the windscreen.

Pilots of RAF Typhoons attacking German armour and vehicles in Normandy in 1944 found that it was difficult to aim the air-to-ground rockets. A number of modifications to the gun/rocket sight and additions to the instruments were progressively introduced. These included a modified reflector sight with a greater depression of the aiming line to allow for rocket 'droop', a more precise low-level altimeter, a more accurate indication of 'skid' and a modified gyro horizon for use as an angle-of-dive indicator.[2]

Radar

One particular instrument not found in production aircraft cockpits in the years leading up to WWII was the CRT (cathode ray tube) used to present radar information. In the previous chapter reference is made to the development of airborne radar which could be used to track an enemy intruder at night. Those who led UK radar development in the late 1930s appreciated quickly that if the *Luftwaffe* used night attacks the position and height data provided by the chain of defence radar stations (CH system) was not accurate enough to enable a controller to position a night fighter within 500 yards of an intruder. Therefore not only had resources to be applied to developing ground controlled interception (GCI) radar but most importantly radar equipment compact, reliable and powerful enough to fit into a night fighter.

In the first few months of war some RAF night fighter Blenheims were fitted with airborne interception (AI) radar. This was operated by a specialist in the back cockpit; some of whom were civilian scientists. The two small diameter CRTs had to be hooded so that the operator could interpret the azimuthal, height and range displays on the CRTs and give the pilot steering information such as 'Turn port ten degrees. Range four thousand'.

By the end of 1940 RAF Fighter Command started to operate the new Beaufighter. This big twin-engine, four 20mm-gun fighter equipped with AI radar soon made night operations over the UK by the *Luftwaffe* very unprofitable. However it would be another two years before the fighter pilot would be able to view directly a CRT in his cockpit and not have to rely completely on the instructions passed to him by the radar operator from the back cockpit.

In the radar-equipped night fighters of WWII we find the origins of the arguments in the post-war decades over the respective merits of single-seat and two-seat interceptors. Rawnsley[3] describes his initial concern when the pilot indicator (PI) for the AI was introduced into Mosquito night fighters. As a highly skilled and experienced radar operator/navigator who 'talked' his pilot into an attacking position he looked on the PI as unnecessary. However he soon came to accept that it enabled the pilot to share some of the workload, as well as speeding up the information link. The PI was one of the precursors of a radar display in the pilot's cockpit.

The *Luftwaffe* and the USN in WWII applied pilot-operated AI to single-seat fighters. The former tried the Neptune series of interception radar in the Bf 109 and the FW 190. The USN used the very successful type APS-4 in the F6F Hellcat. The RAF was not completely convinced that one man could handle an AI radar on his

AI Mk VI radar display unit to the right of the gunsight in an RAF Typhoon. This is an early example of an attack radar in the cockpit of a single-seat fighter.
(Crown copyright)

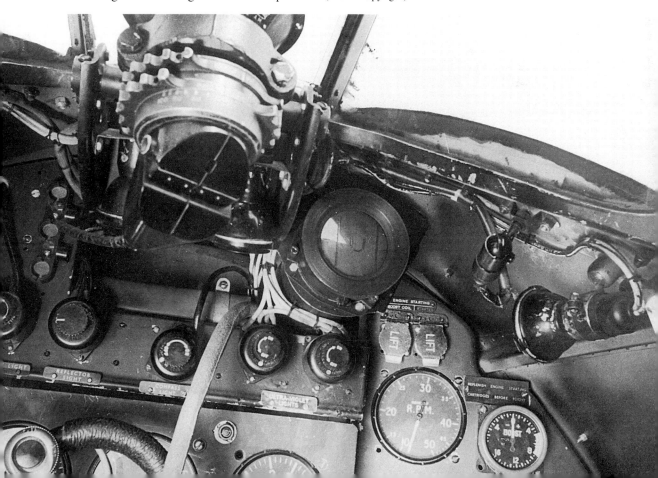

own; although the concept was investigated and flown in a Typhoon.[4]

Rawnsley and Wright in *Night Fighter* provide some of the most revealing and interesting descriptions of the equipment and operating conditions in the cockpits of RAF Fighter Command Beaufighters and Mosquitos. The following extract from *Night Fighter*[5] is an eloquent summary of the tasks of the two men in a night fighter of the 1940s:

'Some of the faith that a night fighter pilot had to have in his navigator in following [an elusive target] might be explained by suggesting that a car owner should try driving a very fast car, with no lights and no brakes, on a dark night down a winding, unlit road close behind another equally fast car with no lights driven by an unarmed desperado who is swerving violently and making unsignalled crash stops. Let the car driver then shut his eyes and keep them shut, and let him rely entirely on his passenger's instructions to keep him out of trouble; and at the same time he must keep closing in on the car he is chasing.'

The work of the radar operator/navigator in a Mosquito fighter was different from that in a Beaufighter. In the latter the second man had to act as loader of the four 20mm guns and operate the AI radar. (Eventually the 20mm guns of the Beaufighter were provided with ammunition 'tanks' to hold disintegrating-link rounds in place of the 60-round drums, as in the Mosquito.) His position did not provide a good vantage point from which to help the pilot during the final visual stage of an interception. Whereas in the Mosquito he could look up from the CRTs of the AI, alongside the pilot, and help to make a visual search of the target through the windscreen. Night vision binoculars were also used. Access to the cockpit of a Mosquito and getting out in a hurry, was through a small door low on the starboard side in the fighter version and under the nose in the bomber version. Pilot and navigator when encased in full flying clothing and equipment were very bulky. They sat shoulder to shoulder. The navigator's small part of the cockpit was crowded with the boxes of the AI

The navigator's side of a Mosquito night fighter with AI Mk X. The small white CRT of the Perfectos Mk II, for homing onto enemy airborne IFF, is set inside the rubber face of the AI visor. Below is the darker CRT of the Monica Mk VIII tail-warning radar which in some aircraft was mounted closer to the pilot's instrument panel.
(Crown copyright)

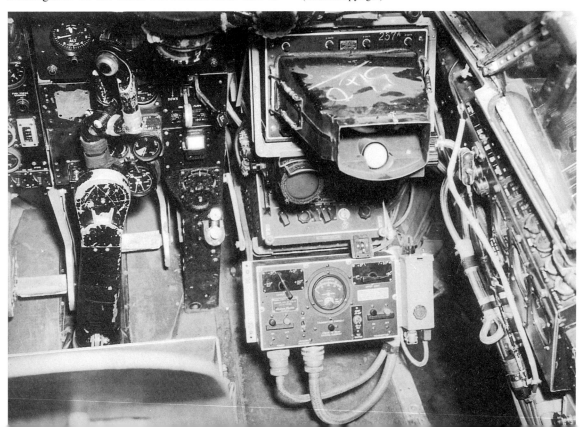

This is believed to show the special Serrate system used by some Mosquitos of RAF Bomber Support night fighters 1944–1945. Serrate was used in conjunction with AI Mk IV to home onto German night fighter radar emissions. The AI's two CRT displays are hidden by the rubber visor. The Monica tail-warning CRT is mounted below the altimeter on the main instrument panel.
(Crown copyright)

radar. To counter high-flying pressurised Ju 86Ps the Mosquito XV was tried. This had a pressurised cabin the entrance to which was through a small double hatch under the nose.

There are many written accounts of flying Mosquitos by surviving aircrew but there are few comments on the type and position of the controls and instruments. This was an era when pilots and others rarely expected that much attention would be given to what we now call ergonomics. In general they got on with the task of flying and put up with awkwardly located and difficult to operate controls. We only need to look at one particular cockpit item in the Mosquito to realise

that convenience dominated the designers' decisions at the drawing board stage. This is the control and indicator box B mounted on the starboard side of the cockpit alongside the navigator's elbow.[6]

Box B was mixture of lamp switches, such as navigation and formation, fuel contents gauges, generator warning light, voltmeter, engine extinguisher controls, clock, instrument lighting control and so on. In other words, Box B was a convenient dumping ground for a miscellaneous collection of items which could not be grouped in a logical arrangement. However, hindsight is a willing slave and therefore it must be recognised that wartime production conditions were not conducive to careful positioning of controls and instruments.

Among the many developments in air interception radars (AIs) one in particular was a precursor of the fighter/attack cockpit in the next decade. This was the projection of the radar CRT display onto the windscreen so that it was reflected into the pilot's forward line-of-sight. In January 1944 a windscreen projecting version of the RAF's AI Mk VIII was developed. This also displayed an artificial horizon. Although this 'head up' attack system could not be perfected for squadron service before the end of the war it was an important step toward the principle of the modern Head-up Display (HUD).

In parallel with radar for RAF Fighter Command, air-to-surface vessel (ASV) radar equipment was developed and went into squadron service with RAF Coastal Command in the first six months of war. It served two principal functions; one, it enabled crews to track surfaced submarines and ships irrespective of visibility and, two, it could be used to 'home' onto a transponder beacon located close to their airfield to make the return from a long over water flight less of a navigational problem.

H2S, Gee and Oboe

First the British, then the Germans and the Americans advanced the technology of airborne radar so that by the end of WWII all the major participating air forces, including the Japanese, equipped their aircraft with one or more radar sets. References to 'in cockpit' radar in Russian aircraft of the time are hard to find. Of all the airborne radar developments H2S was perhaps one of the most significant. It provided the navigators of RAF Bomber Command with a map of the ground and its features and enabled them to direct the aircraft toward and over a selected target area irrespective of the visibility conditions. Other electronic aids which added to the electronics operated by the crew of an RAF bomber included Gee and Oboe. Both of which provided accurate navigational information. Oboe was basically two radar stations which tracked a Pathfinder aircraft and provided a continuous flow of information to enable the pilot and navigator to release marker flares accurately over a selected target and provided continuous control of a Mosquito bomber along an arc which passed directly over a selected target. An aural signal indicated the moment for bomb release.

The increasing effectiveness of the RAF night raids had to be countered by the *Luftwaffe* with airborne radar to supplement the already effective radar-directed guns and searchlights. A typical set was the *Lichtenstein* series. This was fitted in the back cockpit of the night fighter versions of the Me 110 and the Ju 88. The operator monitored three CRT displays. One display showed all targets relative to the aircraft, one the bearing of a selected target and the third the amount the target was above or below the line of flight. By 1943 pilot-operated radars were being fitted to night fighter versions of the FW 190 and the Bf 109; the Neptune series for example.

By the end of WWII aircraft were provided with at least one of the following radars, depending on the aircraft's role: Air-to-surface (ASV); airborne interception (AI); navigational and target-seeking; homing; tail-warning and fire-control for gun turrets. In addition there were systems for electronic intelligence gathering and electronic deception techniques. In less than four years of war electronics had significantly changed the equipment and therefore the appearance of the cockpit.

In the RAF in the last three years of WWII the introduction of electro-mechanical navigational aids, such as the air position indicator (API) based on minutes of latitude and longitude (one minute of latitude equals one nautical mile), hastened the change over to working in nautical miles and speed in knots for all commands and not just Coastal. The Royal and United States Navy's air services have always used the nautical units. However not until the formation of the USAF in 1947 did all American military crews start to use the nautical units.

Simulation

The increasing use of airborne radar systems in the RAF encouraged the development of training devices which simulated the procedures and techniques to be used in flight. At first a Link trainer was modified for use as an airborne interception (AI) radar training device. However, the Link's 'flying' characteristics proved unsuitable for the purpose. The next step was to build a mock up of the cockpit of a night fighter equipped with controls and instruments, radar units and a reflector gun sight. The cockpit was at the focal point of a cyclorama screen on which was projected the image of an enemy aircraft. All systems used for flight, navigation, interception, aiming and firing the guns were included.

Simulators were also developed for training aircrew in the use of Gee and Oboe, ASV and H2S. Dummer[7] records that these devices saved two million actual flying hours and 250 million gallons of fuel.

Better defences

Wireless operator and gunners' positions became more complex as electronic systems proliferated to keep pace with the ever increasing technology of the air war. The British development of power-operated turrets was copied by the Germans and

Interior of an FN5 tail turret of a Wellington bomber. The hydraulic traverse and gun elevation system was controlled by the gunner using the control handles at each side. The reflector gunsight moved in elevation in step with the guns. The linked ammunition was stowed in containers each side of the gunner's seat.
(R. Wallace Clarke)

the Americans, but using guns of 13mm or larger. The RAF was offered turrets mounting 13mm or larger guns but these remained in the minority until the end of WWII. The RAF fitted a gyro sight and gun-laying radar to the four 7.7mm gun tail-turrets of some Lancasters. The tail gunner was also assisted by Fishpond. This was a version of the H2S radar with a plan position indicator on which another crew member could see the relative positions of enemy fighters attempting to approach undetected from below. There was also the tail-warning Monica system. Although they provided a warning their electronic emissions could be detected by *Luftwaffe* night fighters and used as a convenient 'homing' beacon.

Riding with his 'back to the engine' in an FN turret an RAF tail gunner was closely confined by the hydraulic machinery for rotating the turret and elevating the guns. There was a two-hand control grip with dual triggers. Moving in an arc in front of his face was the reflector sight linked to the elevation mechanism. To improve the gunner's chances of spotting an attacking fighter attempting to close in undetected, the Perspex between the guns was removed by some squadrons. This increased the cold-combating task of the gunner's clothing and heated suit.

American power-operated gun turrets were mainly equipped with 13mm guns, but some aircraft had 20mm turrets. The gyro sight was also adopted by the USAAF. The ventral ball turret of the B-17 is an example of one of the most cramped gunner's position. He lay curled up on his back. The two 13mm guns, elevation and traverse mechanisms and the gyro sight, the last between his knees, were crowded into a ball about four feet in diameter. This was another of those claustrophobic locations to be found in many types of military vehicles from tanks through warships to aircraft. Should the turret mechanism be damaged or jam with the guns at zero elevation then the gunner was trapped because the turret doors were not then aligned with the opening in the fuselage. The gunner was very much dependent on other crew members making an attempt to rescue him.

Although the Me 210/410 was intended to emulate and destroy the DH Mosquito it was not a success. The few that entered service soon fell to the guns of the very aircraft they was supposed to master. However, there were a number of clever ideas incorporated into this fast twin-engine two-seat tactical aircraft. One of these was the layout and method of controlling and aiming the 13mm guns which were mounted in barbettes on each side of the fuselage. The gunner, facing aft, was provided with two reflector sights so that he could engage a target on either side. The control grips with triggers moved in the natural sense in relation to the guns.

Gunnery trainers

During WWII the principal air forces made considerable use of gunnery simulators. These ranged from the simple arrangement of a multi-exposure camera mounted on a gun or guns to a ground-based powered turret inside a cyclorama dome with a projected moving target. The complex multi-turret defence system of the B-29, with its remote firing stations and aiming computers, required a correspondingly elaborate and expensive simulator on the ground for training the gunners. As with other simulator systems, it contributed significantly to saving flying hours and fuel.

Crew safety

Fashions in parachutes varied among the air forces of WWII. There were harness fastenings favoured by the British whereby one turn and a bang with the hand released all three parts of the harness, whereas the American harness had three individual release hooks. An innovation adopted by some RAF squadrons was the Irvinsuit which combined a flying coverall with integral harness to which a chest type parachute pack could be fastened. This type of personal safety equipment had the advantage that there were few projections and hooks for catching on equipment when moving about in the cramped conditions of RAF bombers. Crews of B-17s and B-24s were further encumbered by having to wear armoured jackets (flak jackets) and steel helmets when operating through intense German flak and fighter attacks.

Inflatable life rafts, along with inflatable life jackets (MaeWest), provided aircrew with extra assurance that even if the worst were to happen and the aircraft had to ditch, then they stood a second chance of survival. Because life rafts were usually installed in the wings or fuselage there was always the risk that they might inadvertently inflate in flight and damage or obstruct the tail controls.

Armour plating

In the first year of war few aircraft were equipped with armour protection for their crews. As the air war became more intense, pilots in particular were given armoured seats or bulkheads and armour was added to protect other vital parts of the aircraft. The He 111 had an 8mm armoured bulkhead abaft the radio position and 8mm armour also formed the back of the pilot's seat in the Bf 109. On the Bf 109G the windscreen was 90mm thick. A 60mm thick armoured glass windscreen was fitted to the night fighter version of the Bf 110.

The damage inflicted by Bf 109s on Wellington Is in the December 1939 daylight formation sorties to Wilhemshaven highlighted their vulnerability to both 7.7 and 20mm rounds. In subsequent versions of the Wellington an armoured bulkhead was installed abaft the wireless operator's position.

Pressurised crew compartments

Above about 10,000 feet the crew of an aircraft experienced increasing discomfort with every additional 1,000 feet. However, provided they were provided with a regulated supply of oxygen, were in heated cockpits or wore electrically heated suits and did not have to move about too much, or exert themselves, they could retain their effectiveness even when flying at 30,000 feet. At that altitude the air pressure had dropped to 4.4 psi and the outside air temperature was down to around −44 °C. As the airwar developed each of the combatant air forces tried to gain the ascendancy by a number of technological advances. These included higher combat speeds and cruising altitudes above 20,000 feet and above the worst of the weather. Importantly they also made it difficult for an interceptor pilot either to get into an attacking position or hold his aircraft steady enough to aim accurately.

Vickers Wellington VI with pressurised cylindrical cabin for the crew. The pilot sat with his head inside the small transparent dome on top of the fuselage.
(Vickers)

Towards the end of the Battle of Britain in the autumn of 1940 British and German fighters fought above 25,000 feet. Pilots suffered severely from the extreme cold. Just a small hole in the cockpit let in a numbing blast of freezing air. In addition to the discomfort of the cold the windscreen and canopy iced over.[8] The Spitfire had been designed in the mid-1930s for attacking German bombers at around 15,000 feet. The cockpit and the pilot's flying clothing was never intended for an airwar at 30,000 feet and higher. The A&AEE report on the handling tests of the Mk I Spitfire refers to the fact that, although no heating system was provided, the cockpit was kept warm by the heat from the engine and exhaust up to 25,000 feet. Gloves were not needed.[9]

The *Luftwaffe* introduced a pressurised crew compartment for the high altitude P version of the Ju 86 and later for the Ju 388. These were used for photo-reconnaissance. The presence of these aircraft over the UK prompted the development of high altitude interceptors, such as the Welkin, for the RAF. The Wellington V and VI were attempts to develop a high altitude bomber for the RAF. The crew were sealed in a pressurised cylinder with limited external vision and a difficult exit in the event of trouble. Only five high altitude Wellingtons were built and only two went into squadron service but did not prove successful.

None of the British and German methods of providing an acceptable working environment for the crew was entirely satisfactory and in no way was a precursor of the modern pressurised airliner. However in the Boeing B-29 the crew could operate in a virtual shirt-sleeve environment except when attacked or over the target. Three sections of the hull were completely pressurised. The forward and mid sections were connected by a tunnel equipped with a small trolley so that a crew member could propel himself from one to the other. If a crew member happened to be moving in the tunnel between the forward and aft pressurised sections and a window blew out he could be shot like a shell out of a gun. When operating close to a gun defended target area or when attacked by interceptors the B-29 would reduce the pressurisation so as to reduce the effects of being hit. It took a number of incidents when crew members were lost by being sucked out of the aircraft when one of the side fire-control large Perspex blisters blew out before it was made compulsory to wear a parachute at all times and to use a restraining harness. The technology of the pressurised civil Stratocruiser airliner of 1939 applied to the structure of the B-29 showed the way to the pressurisation of civil aircraft after the war.

Emergency flight controls

Some aircraft in WWII with only a one-pilot cockpit were equipped with an emergency set of controls at another crew position. Examples are

---

Aft cockpit of an RAF Havoc (DB-7) night fighter. Against the forward bulkhead are an emergency group of engine controls and a control column which could be 'plugged in' to enable the radar operator to take over from the pilot. At the top is the rubber face piece of the AI Mk IV. The radar unit in the foreground was for training a second operator.
(Crown copyright)

the Martin Maryland and Baltimore and the Douglas DB-7 Boston. The emergency controls of the Maryland and Baltimore were located in the navigator's isolated position in the nose. In the DB-7/Boston the emergency flight and engine controls were in the wireless-operator's position aft. The Martin 139s used by the Netherlands air service in the East Indies in 1941 had a complete set of instruments and controls in the cockpit located at the aft end of the long canopy. These were used by the 2nd pilot/ air gunner during cruising on long flights. One type of French bomber of the 1930s had the second pilot's control position separated and on a different level from that of the first pilot. Presumably this arrangement was intended to avoid both pilots being killed or injured simultaneously.

Windsor

The four-engine Vickers Windsor bomber *c.* 1944 provides another example of cockpit design to which not much thought was given. It provided the pilot with controls arranged to increase his task and to lead to mistakes. The peculiarities of both aircraft and cockpit are remembered by an RAF test pilot seconded to Vickers in 1945. He writes:

'Why a single tail wheel in mid-1945? Why a single-seater fighter [type] cockpit? . . . Much was to be revealed on my first flight. First the single-seater cockpit. Very 'British' after the Liberators. Throttles and pitch controls in your left hand, gear and flaps in your right. Instruments from the Wellington, some gauges first seen before the war in an Audax. Plumbing by the Gas Board, brass cocks and all . . . Look down [from the cockpit] and there was void. Where is the flight engineer and the rest of the crew?? answer, in "caverns measureless to man" and out of sight too.

Approach and landing was easy to do fighter-style, and no need to rumble in from the next county. The only drawback on this time-saving approach was that one was very busy with only one pair of hands . . . changing from throttles and pitch to gear and flaps and quickly back to a left-handful.'[10]

The single pilot's place was difficult to climb up into and just as difficult to vacate in an emergency. Presumably because the RAF had a number of aircraft types having only one pilot's position, irrespective of an aircraft's size, then at 30 tons the Windsor was to be no exception.

More complication

The quest for greater speed, operating height and fire power produced successively more complicated aircraft – the Spitfire XIV, for example. This mark was far in advance of the simple Mk I of the 1930s. The cockpit had more instruments and switches to match the greater performance and an attempt was made to tidy up the proliferation of switches and buttons by mounting them in an orderly row. Although not part of the cockpit nevertheless the Griffon engine in the Mk XIV, with its five-bladed propeller, was far more bulky than the Merlin of earlier marks of Spitfire. This added to the taxying problem of avoiding ground collisions.

The Hawker Tempest was a larger and more potent aircraft than its ancestor the Hurricane but, apart from having more controls and instru-

ments the cockpit was little different from that of the earlier aircraft: the bilges were in full view as were the structural members of the fuselage. A contemporary account of flying the Tempest criticised the cockpit. As in the Hurricane and Typhoon there was no floor to the cockpit. Splayed heel-trays ran from under the seat to each of the rudder pedals and the only inconvenience of not having a floor was in dust, draughts and the possibility of accidentally dropping something. With the seat adjusted for normal pilot height the boost gauge could not easily be seen. The rudder trim control was not to hand and difficult to reach except by the finger tips. The undercarriage lever on the sloping panel on the left was in contact with the calf of the pilot's left

Bristol Beaufighter c. 1945. This illustrates the massive increase in ten years in the number of instruments and controls. The small CRT (to left of the Basic Six panel) is a radar display. (Crown copyright)

leg. The aperiodic magnetic compass, mounted in the traditional RAF position, was masked by the control column.

In addition to inadequate arcs of vision, draughty and unheated and poor cockpit ergonomics in general in many WWII aircraft there were built-in disaster-inducing features. For example, the pilot's seat in the Mosquito was not on the same centre line as the rudder pedals. Not all Mosquito pilots were made aware that the skewed seating posture, which put more weight on one buttock than the other, might induce a false sensation of turning when flying at night or in cloud.

A number of Wellington bombers in WWII dived into the ground at night about three minutes after take-off. At the time the cause was not obvious. In 1949 Professor A.R. Collar investigated the RAF's wartime accidents reports and concluded that the pilots concerned had not been given sufficient instruction in instrument flying. Collar pointed out that, in daylight, a pilot assessed the angle of climb after take-off from the pressure of his back on the seat and his view of the ground. However, on a dark night with few if any lights on the ground a pilot was not always able to tell the difference between a steady climb and acceleration using seat pressure alone.

At the top of climb out, when the aircraft was levelled out, there was an increase in speed. This gave a sensation of pressure on the pilot's back which might lead to the assumption that the aircraft was still climbing. Therefore the pilot would push the control column forward to achieve as he thought level flight. In a circle of cause and effect the aircraft might be pushed over into a fatal dive.

A better pilot's place

Few of the aircraft design offices in WWII had the resources or time to allow in-depth studies of what we now call human factors or ergonomics in the control interface such as the cockpit. Attempts were made by some designers to improve the control interface. There were many cockpit layouts proposed by pilots who, after all, were in the best position to comment based on the experience of sitting for many hours in dis⁻

comfort, unable to obtain accurate instrument readings or employ safe instrument scanning techniques, unable to see ahead clearly in precipitation and so on. One designer in particular made a big effort in this respect. This was Martin-Baker's MB V which was not only one of the most advanced of all piston-engined aircraft, it had a cockpit in which ergonomic considerations had been applied.

The designer of the MB V was unconstrained by tradition. He included many new ideas for the structure, the fitting of the instrument panel and

FW 190. Time and money appear to have been no object when it came to the details of the instruments, panels and switches. The overall finish and layout is very tidy and the 'bilges' are not in sight. Alongside the REVI gunsight are the round counters for the guns.
(P. Jarrett)

Martin-Baker with the MB V produced a cockpit in which much thought was given to the layout of instruments and controls. The result was an example for other designers to follow.
(Martin-Baker)

Although the DH Hornet fighter arrived too late for WWII nevertheless the cockpit is representative of the era. The reflector gunsight uses the windscreen as a combining glass off which to reflect the aiming images. This is tidier than most British cockpits of the time and the 'bilges' are not in view.
(British Aerospace)

access panels in the fuselage and wings. The cockpit was no exception. He started with a clean sheet of paper. Whereas Camm of Hawkers and others figuratively looked over their shoulder at the cockpits that had gone before. In contrast the cockpit of the MB V had few 'odd corners' into which loose objects might hide. The instruments and controls were in orderly arrays and anticipated the fighter cockpits of a later generation.

Films

For ninety or more years the aircraft cockpit has featured in fictional writing and in films. However, its equipment is usually ignored. In the typical aviation novel the pilot, more often than not, leaps into the cockpit and within a few lines the aircraft is up among the clouds. Attendant mechanics and the need, even in a WWI fighter, for some manipulation of the engine controls and fuel system are ignored. Engine starting has rarely been a 'leap into the cockpit and press a button' type of exercise. It has usually required some deliberate sequence of actions and required some time. This is of course anathema to the thriller writer or film maker: just as in railway fiction and film the reality of safety devices, such as continuous 'fail-safe' brakes, have been ignored lest the facts spoilt a good story.

The depiction of the cockpit in book and film is mentioned at this stage because WWII generated millions of words and feet of film on the subject. Korda's *The Lion Has Wings* of late 1939 is among a host of aviation films in which the producer and director never let the facts get in the way of the story. Korda's film, when seen today, is, as was intended, 100% propaganda. The RAF pilots and aircrew wear white or light coloured flying clothing. The *Luftwaffe* crews are in all-over black; including their scowls. The cockpit shots in an RAF Wellington are reasonably accurate. However when the same cockpit serves for that of a *Luftwaffe* bomber the film is reversed so as to position the pilot on the right. The forward and tail gun Frazer Nash turrets are seen whenever newsreel shots of real Wellingtons are shown but the studio re-creation of the gunners' positions suggest that the Wellington only had manually controlled Lewis guns.

One of the most obvious changes made to facilitate filming occurred among American fighter cockpits. These were usually depicted as being extraordinarily roomy. Although the cockpits of American fighters were larger than those of other nations they were nowhere as large as those of the Hollywood mockups of cockpits. Hollywood had an advantage over other film centres in that American pilots usually used a throat microphone and therefore the star's features were not hidden by a face mask microphone.

One item in particular which was rarely depicted correctly on film before about 1950 was the fighter gun sight. Some remarkable devices were thought up by the property departments. In *Captains of the Clouds* (Warner Brothers 1942) a lone German fighter somehow is able to navigate and find a formation of Hudson bombers on their way across the Atlantic. Despite the fact that illustrations of the standard *Luftwaffe* reflector sight were to be found in many aviation publications Hollywood chose to ignore the fact.

Safely down

During WWII, particularly in Britain and the USA, methods were sought for guiding aircraft automatically to a safe touchdown. Although by the last two years of war electronic aids to navigation had removed much of the uncertainty over finding an airfield, nothing much had been done about the final two or three miles leading to the threshold of the runway. The RAF wanted a system which would ensure the speedy recovery of large numbers of bombers in reduced visibility conditions. The Lorenz beam approach system was one of a number of radio aids to both navigation and landing developed in Germany from the mid-1920s onward. The RAF also used a version. The system required great concentration on the part of the pilot to use effectively. A tired crew and a damaged aircraft attempting a landing in low visibility conditions required a more precise and easier-to-use system. The FIDO equipment installed on the extra long emergency runways was one answer. Burning great quantities of fuel along each side of the runway dispersed fog. However, it was installed at only one or two RAF stations.

Development of military autoland systems continued after the war; especially for the RAF's V bomber force. The research was eventually extended to include civil passenger-carrying aircraft operations. With approach and landing speeds increasing, sometimes by as much as 50% and the need to maintain operational effectiveness irrespective of the visibility, the development of automatic landing was pushed ahead. Not until after the war did the Royal Aircraft Establishment (RAE) in Britain perfect vastly improved systems

The C-47/ Dakota /DC-3 cockpit is typical of American transport aircraft instruments and controls of the 1940s: albeit this is a post-war version with additional instruments including a Sperry Zero Reader.
(British Airways)

of approach and runway lighting (e.g. the Calvert). These gave the pilot the maximum guidance during a landing in poor visibility conditions. Had they been available in WWII they would have reduced the number of landing incidents and accidents arising from faster approach speeds and aircraft which were larger and less manoeuvrable. Research into aircrew fatigue, particularly that of pilots, was an important subject in WWII. The Cambridge Cockpit studies in which pilots 'flew' a Spitfire simulator produced data on the effects of long exposure to noise, aircraft movement and concentration on instruments. Not unexpectedly the commonly perceived deterioration in skill after many hours in the cockpit was verified by the results. Specific end deterioration is a human

condition that has been the cause of many approach and landing accidents. At the end of a long and arduous flight there is a natural tendency to relax: 'We've made it back. We'll be on the ground in a few minutes.' The modern motorist is a frequent victim of specific end deterioration; as highlighted by the incidence of accidents close to a driver's home.

'Contact' flying

Earlier reference was made to 'contact' flying, particularly in the USA. In WWII aircrews, American and European, who trained in the USA and Canada became accustomed to the 'chessboard' appearance of the terrain. The regular pattern of fields and roads along with clearly defined railway lines and rivers simplified navigation. Also, the more predictable weather was an advantage. In contrast the visibility for much of the time in the United Kingdom, to which the new crews graduated, was poor. The visibility could change significantly during the time it took to take off, circle the airfield and commence an approach to a landing. Their navigation and airmanship tasks included 'reading' the confused ground pattern of small fields, villages, narrow twisting lanes and streams and numerous railway lines. Adding to their problems was the standard RAF arrangement of station buildings and hangers. From the air one station looked like another, particularly in East Anglia. Therefore special 'European familiarisation' schools had to be established.

Another type of 'contact' flying and one which was often made very difficult because of the cockpit type and position, was that of finding an aircraft carrier and landing on it. Deck landings had always been hazardous and they were made more dangerous with the introduction of high-performance fighters and torpedo bombers into the US and Royal Navies. Keeping the carrier in view during the down wind leg of the landing pattern when flying a Corsair, for example, took discipline and skill. There was always the possibility of experiencing a form of vertigo if the pilot looked to the left at the ship for too long. After turning from the base leg and aligning with the deck the landing attitude of this long-nosed fighter deprived the pilot of any direct view

ahead. The same problem was found with other aircraft when adapted for carrier work; such as the Spitfire. In poor visibility much of the landing pattern was flown on instruments. Only when close to touching down could a view be had of the deck and then it might not be aligned in the expected position. All the time the pilot had to avoid letting the aircraft get too fast or too slow, climb or descend, reduce power or increase power too much. The last thing the pilot wanted was a view of the landing signals officer's instructions shared with the engine and the frames of the windscreen.

G-suits

By the end of WWII the air forces on both sides had developed many different technologies aimed at improving the lethality and versatility of aircraft. Engines, electronics and weapons had made a massive leap up the curve of advancing technology. One particular technique which came in the last year of war would become of increasing importance with the advent of aircraft able to impose much higher G loads on their structures than those of the previous generation of combat aircraft.

Higher G loads also meant high G effects on aircrew. The pilots of high performance fighters were frequently experiencing what we now call G-LOC (Loss Of Consciousness because of G). The USAAF developed the G-3A suit. This enabled pilots of P-51s, for example, to 'pull' seven G without blacking out. The suit automatically inflated to exert pressure on the pilot's abdomen, thighs and calves at 2-G and increased its pressure in step with a further increase in G.

Cockpit design and the development of interface equipment continued at a steady pace right up to the final day of WWII. Research into aircraft having better performance and versatility still included the concept of human aircrew. In the preceding five years much had been learnt about human behaviour. However, much of what had been learnt and which might have improved cockpits could not be applied because of the pressure of war. Among the data on human performance are the following gathered by the USAAF[11]: Of 460 accidents and incidents classified as 'pilot error' 50% were attributed to confusing one control with another; 18% to operating a control incorrectly; 18% to failure to check, unlock or operate a control; 11% arose from adjustment errors; and 3% because the pilot could not reach a control.

Sometimes these facts were carried forward to the design of the next generation of aircraft. Sometimes they were not.

Notes

1. Currie, J. (1983) *Mosquito Victory*, p. 17. Goodall.
2. AIR 20/3592, PRO.
3. Rawnsley, C.F. & Wright, R. (1957) *Night Fighter*, Collins.
4. Gunston, W.D. (1990) *Avionics*, Patrick Stephens.
5. Rawnsley & Wright *op cit*.
6. AP2019 B, G & K Vol. I HMSO.
7. Dummer, G. (1996 April–June) *Air Mail*, pp12, 13.
8. Flint, P. (1996) *Dowding and HQ Fighter Command*, p. 142. Airlife.
9. Price, A. *ed*. (1995) *The Spitfire Story*, p. 59. Arms and Armour.
10. Stones, D. (1986 Nov) *FLYPAST*, p. 43.
11. *Air Force Magazine* (1947, Nov).

CHAPTER FIVE
1945 – c.1990

Jet propulsion

Jet and rocket aircraft only made the last year of WWII. The Me 262 and other jets of the *Luftwaffe* pointed the way ahead. They were ahead of their time, or rather the technologies of the gas turbine and the rocket were ahead of airframe and system technologies. The development engineers on both sides of the war had to concentrate on proving the aircraft gas turbine as a prime mover. Research into high speed wing sections and swept-back wings, to delay the onset of aerodynamic problems of flight close to Mach One, was well advanced in Germany but less so in Britain and America. Therefore the British Gloster Meteor, for example, was a conventional twin-engine, un-swept wing, fighter with turbines in place of piston-engines. There was neither the time nor the resources to be concerned overmuch with instrument and systems design. Therefore the introduction of the gas turbine propulsion system did not have an immediate effect on the design and equipment of cockpits in general: apart from turbine temperature indicators reading up to 1,000°C and rpm indicators graduated from 0 to 15,000 rpm.

Instrument panel for the Vampire jet fighter c. 1947. Apart from the rpm indicator reading up to 10,000, cabin pressure indicator and five fuel contents gauges this could be a contemporary piston-engine aircraft panel.
(Smiths Industries)

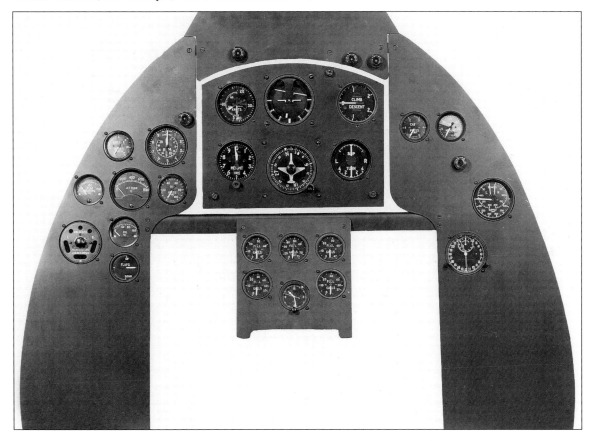

The effect of jet aircraft developments in the mid-40s on cockpit design and equipment applied mainly to details. The general shape of fighter and fighter/bomber cockpits remained very much in the style of the current piston-engine aircraft. Eventually the need for ejection seats required some changes to the basic 'piston-engine' cockpit.

The Arado 234 design positioned the pilot in the extreme nose without the all-round vision of a bubble canopy. The full-throttle speed of the AR 234 was about 400 knots; that of the Tempest and Meteor of the RAF was about 360 knots. Perhaps the speed margin of the Arado 234 enabled the designer to assume that he could dispense with an all-round vision tear-drop, drag-producing canopy because it was going to be difficult for anyone to make a surprise stern attack.

The Me 163 *Komet* rocket propelled fighter had a cockpit that was even more of a death-trap for the pilot than the Sopwith Dolphin of 1917. It was not just a matter of not being able to escape quickly in the event of trouble or a crash: it was the knowledge that the cockpit was surrounded by the T-Stoff (hydrogen-peroxide) fuel tank. If the T-Stoff escaped the pilot would be literally eaten alive. The pilot of an Me 163 also made every approach to landing knowing that he had to make a precision touchdown with a skid, instead of a normal shock-absorbing undercarriage, otherwise a heavy landing and bounce might fracture his spine.

The principal instrument panel in front of the pilot of an Me 262 had the primary flight instruments offset to the left of the centre line and with the engine instruments to the right. The flight instruments were arranged in two rows with, from left to right in the top row, airspeed, artificial horizon with integral turn-and-bank and vertical speed; in the bottom row were the altimeter, remote indicating compass and the indicator for the 'Y' range and bearing system. The 'Y' System combined an aircraft's RT transmissions with the ground-based *Heinrich* DF and the omni-directional *Wotan* stations to produce a left-right indication to guide the pilot to a target or to an airfield. The array of engine indicators included, for both engines, rpm, fuel injection pressure, jet pipe temperature and oil pressure. Above the main panel was the REVI 16B reflector sight.

The general appearance of the cockpit was of a tidy and logical layout. However, things were somewhat different when starting the engines. Like some other aircraft of the decade, starting the Me 262 was a complex, two-handed, series of actions. After the required switches had been set the pilot used his right hand to push down the starter lever of the selected engine and then, if the two-stroke starter motor fired, the lever was pulled up and held until the main engine reached 2,000 rpm. Alongside the starter lever was a button which selected a low-reading scale on the rpm indicator. As the main engine rpm reached 1,000 the pilot's left hand pressed the ignition button on the throttle lever until the fuel burners lit and rpm reached 3,000. Above 3,000 rpm the throttle could be opened and the starter motor lever on the other side of the cockpit released. At the same time the right hand could release the low-rpm button and transfer to the main fuel cock lever on the left. But this was not the end; the right hand had to go back to the other side to reset the rpm indicator to its normal scale of readings. Throughout the operation each step in the sequence had to be made at a specified rpm or on successful completion of the previous action. Having started one of the two Jumo 004B-2s, the same procedure had to be gone through for the other. All the early jet engines had to be treated carefully and, above all, rapid throttle movements had to be avoided otherwise the engine might flame-out.

The Gloster Meteor, the first large scale production jet aircraft fighter for the RAF, introduced an entirely new cockpit environment. The most notable feature was the absence of the low frequency vibrations and sounds which many pilots had endured when flying Tempests and Spitfires and other piston-engine aircraft. No longer was the view ahead shared with a bulky radial or in-line engine. In the Meteor the pilot had a virtually unobstructed view ahead from the cockpit which was set close to the nose of the aircraft. Adding to the excellent visibility from the cockpit when taxying was the level ground attitude provided by the nosewheel undercarriage.

In contrast to, say the Me 262, the starting check list for the engines of the Meteor consisted

The left side of the cockpit of DH Vampire showing (white) the twist grip on the throttle lever by which the pilot fed the target range into the gyro gunsight.
(British Aerospace)

of only seven lever and button selection steps. However, in 1945 the turbine engine was still in its infancy and therefore care had to be exercised so as not to allow the jet pipe temperature to reach an excessive value, usually around 500°C. The pilot also had to keep the rpm for each engine away from a value at which the jet pipe resonated to such an extent that it caused the turbine to shed blades.

The Meteor is another example of design office priorities. Although the gas turbine engine in both Germany and Britain was under development in the 1930s the many problems to be overcome, particularly the metallurgical, delayed the introduction of a practicable jet aircraft until near the end of WWII. Gloster Aircraft, both with its

experimental jet and the subsequent Meteor, was not able to devote too much time and resources to detailed refinements of the latter's airframe, which was essentially that of a conventional twin piston-engine aircraft. The cockpit and its equipment had to be provided from what was available. Therefore the cockpit of the Meteor was little different from those of the piston-engine fighters. The most notable difference, apart from the good forward arcs-of-view and the level ground attitude, was with the engine instrumentation. The rpm indicators had a top limit mark of 10,000 compared with the 3000 rpm of a piston-engine and instead of coolant temperature gauges there were jetpipe temperature indicators reading up to 1,000°C.

The price paid for the speed potential of the Meteor, as with other jet aircraft, was a fuel consumption much greater than that of a piston engine aircraft. This meant that among the cockpit instruments those concerned with fuel

DH Vampire T-11 trainer of the 1950s. 'The back of the clockmaker's shop'.
(British Aerospace)

flow and quantity were of vital importance. Although incidental to cockpit design, the Meteor pilot had to avoid 'idling' on the ground and at all times had to keep 'one eye' on the fuel quantity remaining and pay strict attention to the 'Bingo' radio reminders from the ground that 'his time was up'. The Derwent engines of the Meteor Mk IV, for example, burnt around 200 gallons of kerosene each hour of flight. Even when taxying to the take-off point each engine used 20 gallons. With only 325 gallons total fuel only 60 gallons might remain at the end of a sortie up to 40,000 feet with which to complete an approach to the airfield and landing and allow for a 'wave off' and a go round again circuit.

Apart from those related to the turbine engines the type and arrangement of the instruments were typical RAF *c*.1944. The early marks of the Meteor had the RAF Basic Six panel set below the gyro gunsight. Successive developments of the basic Meteor design, such as the AW NF 11 two-seat night fighter, exhibited a number of differences in cockpit equipment related to the role of the aircraft. For example the Mk IV and later types had pressurised cockpits along with the warning in the Pilot's Notes not to throttle back too much at high altitude thereby losing cockpit pressure.

At the time when the Meteor, with its unswept wings, represented the first-line strength of RAF Fighter Command, the USAF was given the North American F-86 Sabre. Its swept wings owed much to the aerodynamic developments of German scientists whose knowledge and research results were used as a guide by North American. It was for its time the best of the breed and gave the Communist MiG 15 pilots over Korea a nasty shock.

The cockpit of the F-86 was more cramped than the usual American type because the six 13mm guns were mounted in threes on each side of the fuselage. One comment on the instrument layout said that: 'In the tradition of American fighters the instrument layout was neat and logical in presentation.' That may have applied to the F-86, but not to the F-86D which had a big radar CRT on the main instrument panel, resulting in a somewhat untidy layout. However, the contention that American instrument panels were, in general, 'neat and logical', may be challenged. They may have been neat but, as later research in America showed, they were not always logically arranged.[1]

The importance of the F-86 to the history of the fighter cockpit was in the protection afforded the pilot: there was an ejection seat; the pilot wore a G-suit and there was alloy and steel armour plating in front of and behind the pilot. The F-86 entered service with the USAF equipped with a Mk 18 gyro gunsight which contributed to the shooting skills of the American pilots.

With increased performance, particularly for fighters, came heavy flight control loads. These had to be reduced by adding power-assistance. However, the early system was the cause of many problems. What happened if the power system failed? The usual arrangement was a direct mechanical linkage from the control column to the control surfaces, along with a means to keep the stick loads within the pilot's muscular ability. In the F3D-1 a very simple solution was devised. At the press of a button, the control column could be extended upwards. This increased the leverage of the stick so that the pilot could cope with the control loads.

The F3D-2 had the G-3 autopilot. The autopilot control panel included a small control stick for making limited manoeuvres and a levelling button which returned the aircraft to level flight from any attitude of climb, glide and bank up to 65 degrees. There was also a button for selecting barometric altitude hold.

Among the fighters of the 1950s the F4D is another example of the way in which cockpit design lagged behind other advances in technology. The delta-wing Douglas F4D was not a good aircraft. The control system lacked harmony; the afterburner was erratic in operation; the air intakes were aerodynamically not matched to the engine; the free-floating leading edge slats did not work when they should; and there were other failings. The instruments and controls in the cockpit were neither arranged nor designed to meet the demands of an aircraft intended as a night and all-weather fighter. An experienced United States Navy pilot expressed himself in no uncertain terms when writing about the F4D:

> 'All-weather flying implies much headwork by the pilot and a lot of reference to charts, displays, radios, lights and switches. The F4D cockpit was jammed and crammed. Most switches were haphazardly located. Most of the instruments were grossly misplaced. Light reflections danced round the multifaceted windscreen and canopy like lights in a discotheque. The autopilot, which could have been a godsend to the harried pilot, never worked. The airplane was just as happy flying on its side as it was flying upright. The afterburner lit with a bang that curdled your buttocks and the control stick was short, stubby, hesitant, halting, heavy, jerky in motion and almost completely obscured the radar scope.'[2]

The quoted description includes many examples of poor cockpit ergonomics in the cockpit of the F4D. But they were not unique to that aircraft. Many could be applied to the cockpits of other fighters of the 1950s and 60s.

Canberra bomber c. 1950. Externally the aircraft had the clean lines of a typical jet bomber/fighter. However, inside the cockpit things were rather different and were back in the WWII piston-engine era with a place for everything and everything in any place.
(British Aerospace)

Jet bombers

When it came to the B-47 jet bomber Boeing departed from the traditional American flight deck layout for bombers. In place of the standard side-by-side, two-pilot arrangement the B-47 had tandem cockpits under one transparent canopy similar to that of a fighter aircraft. Another interesting departure from tradition for pilot and gangway layouts was the positioning of the gangway to the left of the seats rather than to the right. A similar gangway position was adopted for the B-45 Tornado of the USAF; the first of which flew in the same year, 1947, as the B-47. The prototype B-52 had a tandem cockpit but Boeing reverted to the traditional, side-by-side, for the production series. A distinguishing feature of the central control pedestal was the eight throttles. The pilots of the earlier Convair B-36 even had to get their hands around ten throttles.

Multi-role cockpits

Since the start of military aviation few aircraft types have been used exclusively in the role for which they were first conceived. For example, the single-seat biplane fighters of WWI, such as the Camel, were eventually equipped to carry bombs and extra guns for the strafing of troops in the trenches.

Between wars air forces often have to adapt aircraft to perform more than one operational

role because nations usually do not like spending money on armaments. The 'general purpose' appellation has been used to embrace high- and low-level bombing, reconnaissance, ground attack and photo-reconnaissance. During WWII most of the new types among the agile, as opposed to heavy bombers, acquired new functions as the airwar reduced the need for the pure interceptor. In the last year of war over Europe the American and British air forces deployed some of their fastest and best fighters in close-support of the advancing armies. The one-time 'fighter-only' pilots had to acquire the additional skills of low-level attack. In WWI many RFC pilots looked on ground attack sorties as both dangerous and not the sort of flying for which they had volunteered.

Saab A-21 twin-boom jet fighter. The gyro gunsight, with its prominent pilot's face protection pad, and the frames of the windscreen limited the forward arcs of view. The A-21, even in its earlier piston-engine version, had an ejection seat.
(Saab AB)

The shape and equipment of the cockpit of aircraft adapted to additional or new roles however did not change significantly. A few more switches for bomb and rocket selection were added and the gyro gunsight modified to allow for the greater drooping trajectory of rockets compared with shells. Aircraft that originally had been designed to fight at 20,000 feet or higher were now directed by forward air controllers onto the enemy's armoured formations moving on the ground. Unfortunately there were 'blue-on-blue' incidents when aircraft attacked their own side because of poor communication, inadequate briefing or just the inability to distinguish between friend and foe among the confusion of the land battle. The experience of the airwar over Europe in the later stages of the war were to have a great influence on both the design of future aircraft and on cockpit equipment and design.

In the 1950s increasing attention was being paid to the need for aircraft whose primary function was that of strike or 'ground attack'. The airwar of the future was envisaged as being in two parts: one close to the stratosphere; the other close to the 'nap' of the earth. The latter predicated aircraft with a cockpit interface able to convey to the pilot far more information then before. More and higher quality information could only be acquired by adding more and more electronic sensors, such as radar, and in consequence more and more displays and controls in the cockpit. The greater complexity also resulted in vast increases in aircraft cost which in turn required more rigorous pilot training programmes so as to make the best possible use of what were being termed 'weapon systems'; rather than an aircraft to which weapons were 'add-ons'.

Too many cooks

In the early 1960s the USAF wanted to operate the General Dynamics F-111 primarily as a precision bomber and not as a fighter. But the USN wanted the twin-engine, two-seat, variable-geometry F-111 as a fleet defence fighter. Both services were ordered by the Pentagon to aim for a common aircraft which would meet both operational roles. Along the way the major problem of the cockpit and its profile entered the design

process and was influenced by subsequent arguments and contrary decisions among the two services. The navy wanted the pilot and navigator/electronics operator seated side-by-side, whereas the air force wanted the traditional tandem seat arrangement.

General Dynamics produced the F-111 (USAF) with side-by-side seating in a cockpit which was part of an escape capsule. The pilot had a limited view aft and to the right. Aerodynamic and structural considerations precluded a canopy proud of the top line of the fuselage. Of course, the air force intended to use the aircraft as a bomber and to rely on speed for defence therefore there was less need for a view astern. Even had the air force or the navy wanted a raised canopy, so as to improve the all-round view, the serious transonic drag problems that beset the aircraft's progress from prototype to production aircraft ruled out any changes to the original cockpit profile. As it happened the navy lost interest in the F-111 as a fleet defence fighter or for any other role.

In the late 1960s the F-111's instruments were updated and a mission management system installed which took charge of most of the navigation, communication and target seeking and attacking tasks from the crew. A key element in the update was a digital computer and a new multi-function radar. The crew of an F-111 can see the ground mapped and displayed with accuracy and clarity on the display screens in the cockpit. They can distinguish between stationary and moving targets on the ground. The sensor/display system also provides guidance for air-to-air missiles should the F-111 have to take part in a dogfight, despite its primary role as a bomber.

Perhaps the most important item in the F-111's avionics and one which affects directly the crew's handling of the aircraft is the terrain following radar. This reduces crew workload particularly when flying at 500 feet or less at 500 knots. At that level and speed any hesitation or slow reaction on the part of the pilot could lead to disaster. The F-111's terrain following system keeps the aircraft at a constant pre-selected height above the earth's surface particularly when it is rugged and undulating.

105

Navigator's station

By the end of WWII Allied bomber and transport aircraft navigators were provided with a number of electronic aids, such as Gee, Loran and Decca. These along with improved air position indicators and radio position fixing remained in use for at least the next ten years. However, by about 1960 the USAF started to fit inertial navigation systems and other air forces followed. In addition radio and radar Doppler ground speed measuring techniques helped to improve further the accuracy of navigation. Air force navigators increasingly became operators of sophisticated avionic systems. In fighter/attack aircraft they also looked after much of the target seeking avionics.

Flight engineer's station

Some aircraft types of WWII and for the next twenty years or more were large and had so many complex systems needing continuous monitoring that a specialist crew member was carried. In the RAF Lancaster four-engine bombers the position to the right of the pilot was occupied not by a

second pilot but by the flight engineer. In the American B-17s and B-24s the management of engines and systems was shared between the second pilot and an engineer/gunner. The second pilot's instrument panel mounted all the engine indicators. The B-29, with a greater number of systems to be monitored, required a dedicated flight engineer's station.

A typical flight engineer's tasks of this period included responsibility for the pre-flight checks. These might cover over a 100 items and included ensuring that the fuel on board was sufficient for the forthcoming sortie. The flight engineer also determined at what point in the flight fuel needed to be transferred from one set of tanks to another. With the crew on board the engineer assisted the captain in going through the engine start routine. During take-off he followed the captain's hand on the throttles as they were opened to full power. At

The flight engineer's station in an RAF Nimrod maritime patrol aircraft from which the majority of the systems are monitored and controlled.
(Smiths Industries)

the same time he watched closely the vital engine instrument ready to warn of a failure. After take-off the engines were set to climb power and then on reaching cruising level adjusted to maintain the aircraft at the speed demanded by the navigator. At frequent intervals the fuel remaining was calculated so that the navigator could keep his 'Howgozit' graph up to the minute. (A 'Howgozit' graph plotted planned and actual fuel consumption against time.)

During the cruise phase of a sortie the flight engineer made frequent small adjustments to the engine controls to keep them synchronised at the desired rpm. Throughout a flight, variations in air density and temperature had an effect on the engines which had to be compensated for. The engineers in the B-29s of the USAAF operating at maximum range across the Pacific to raid Japan performed a vital function; particularly if an aircraft had been damaged when hundreds of miles from its island base.

An engineer's dedicated position with instruments and controls introduces the subject of the advantages and disadvantages of not sitting facing forward. When sitting forward and with the instruments and controls arranged from left to right to match the general relationship of the major parts of the aircraft there is less chance of a mistake being made. But when facing aft the starboard engines, for example, are to the engineer's left. Despite this ergonomic anomaly there were many aircraft types in which the flight engineer faced aft.

Human protection

The extreme altitude aircraft of WWII, such as the Wellington V and the pressurised cabin version of the Ju 86, had provided very little specialised protection for the crew in the event of trouble. Special versions of the Spitfire had pressurised cockpits to permit sustained operation at extreme altitude. The air pressure in the cockpit of the Spitfire VI at 37,000 feet was equivalent to that at 28,000 feet altitude. As the pressurising air supply was warmed the temperature was kept at 8°C even when the outside temperature was down to minus 42°C. However, this was not a true pressure cabin within the general meaning because the difference

between the outside pressure and that inside the cockpit was only about 2 psi. The compressor driven by the R-R Merlin 47 could provide only just enough volume of air to overcome the leakage through the numerous small holes.[3]

The advent of the jet aircraft introduced many more problems associated with life support and safety. Among the many 'trade-offs' or compromises and often difficulty of having to choose between one solution and another was that of providing environmental protection for the human crew. The basic question that had to be answered was: provide special life-supporting garments or provide a pressurised cabin? The first solution encased a crew member in a helmet and a bulky pressurised suit which included a parachute. The second answer posed many structural and space problems for the aircraft designer; but it did permit a 'shirtsleeve' environment for the crew. A typical cabin pressure would have been equivalent to 10,000 feet. Modern civil passenger aircraft keep the cabin at about 8,000 feet.

The final year of war ushered in an entirely new era of aircrew protection and comfort. Up to then only experimental test aircrew and high altitude research crews had been given specialised life support equipment. Only the B-29 crews had experienced a significant number of flights at high altitudes in pressurised compartments. Fighter and bomber crews wore parachute harness and oxygen masks but little else to improve their chances of survival in the event of trouble. But things were changing and ejection seats, personal life-support clothing and protective 'bone dome' helmets gradually became the standard; albeit the first generation of jet-fighter pilots continued to wear the 'soft' helmets of the piston-engine days. In 1954 RAF pilots of Vickers Supermarine Swift jet fighters still wore the 'soft' helmet of the piston-engine era.

Even before the jet age, pilots were sometimes severely injured by 'bird strikes' which smashed through the windscreen and injured the pilot. The 'bone dome' and its visor became an essential item of wear particularly when flying at high speed close to the ground. For example, a SEPECAT Jaguar flying at 460 knots at 200 feet hit a bird. The windscreen was penetrated and the combining glass of the Head-Up Display was smashed. Fortunately the pilot's helmet visor was down and he was not injured.

Sound intensity

The demise of the piston engine for first line military aircraft removed the hazard of carbon monoxide fumes in the cockpit. The jet engine's exhaust contained only a small mount of CO and was well away from the cockpit. Piston engine rpm rarely exceeded 3,000 whereas even the first generation gas turbines could reach 10,000 rpm so that the pilot was subjected to a different range of frequencies and intensities. As comparative examples there are the sound level of 120 decibels at piston-engine frequencies in the cockpit of the USN's F-4U and the 120 decibels at much higher frequencies affecting the crew of a jet-engined B-45. Irrespective of the variations of sound intensity among different aircraft types the key figure is that of 140 decibels above which both air and ground crew will suffer from disorientation and nausea unless wearing ear sound protectors.[4] One hundred decibels imposed continuously for eight hours eventually causes hearing loss.[5] In both piston and turbine engine aircraft the inter-com system not only relays speech, radio and audio warnings, it generates noise. Unwanted noise distorts information and keeps the sound level dangerously high.

The ejection seat

When normal operating airspeeds began to increase above 450 knots mechanically assisted means of escape, such as ejection seats, had to be developed. Ejection seats were developed and fitted to aircraft in Germany in the closing stages of WWII. The test pilot in the He 280V1 who found that suddenly he had no control of the aircraft was among the first to use an ejection seat 'in anger'. This was on 13 August 1942. The compressed air-operated seat was the first of a number developed for the *Luftwaffe*'s final generation of aircraft: the He 162 jet and the piston-engine Do 335 *Pfeil* for example: but the Me 262 did not have an ejection seat for the pilot. In 1943 the Saab J 21A fighter, twin-boom, pusher-propeller engine arrangement, was fitted with an ejection seat to shoot the pilot clear of the

propeller. The Meteor and Vampire were designed with conventional pilot seats. In the event of trouble the pilot had to roll the aircraft inverted, jettison the canopy and drop out and make a normal parachute departure.

After 1945 the frontiers of altitude and speed were pushed further and further outward as engine and airframe developments were advanced. The USAF was allocated massive financial and material resources for the development of super-sonic and stratospheric aircraft. In relation to cockpit development this programme included studying an He 162 seat and the work of Martin-Baker in Britain. Both improved ejection seats

Martin-Baker Mk 14 ejection seat for the USN. The 'firing' handle is between the pilot's legs. The legs will be pulled back by the straps before the seat gun fires. (Martin-Baker)

and environmental protection for pilots followed. It was in this particular era of aviation that emerged the concept of the escape capsule.

Air staff requirements in the late 1940s, particularly in the UK, included: 'In the last resort a reasonable means of escape in an emergency must be provided for the crew.' Until the advent of the jet fighter the safety and recovery of aircrew was assured by the provision of escape hatches, jettisonable cockpit hoods and blast deflection devices.

Outside Germany the pioneer in reliable and practical ejection seats which could be fitted to a wide range of aircraft was James Martin (later Sir James) of Martin-Baker Ltd. The company's records show that the need for escape devices was not confined to jet aircraft because both the Spitfire and the Hurricane were the subject of research into ways of assisting a pilot to abandon aircraft. As early as October 1944 a swinging-arm, pilot-ejection system was demonstrated in model form to the Ministry of Aircraft Production. Later a full size system was tested in

a Defiant and a number of successful flights were made in which a dummy was swung out and up from the aircraft on the end of an arm pivoted near the fin and assisted by a compressed spring.

Following the lead set by Germany, Martin-Baker decided that the best way of projecting aircrew clear of an aircraft in an emergency would be by the forced ejection of the seat using an explosive charge. James Martin had to consider the sudden loads imposed on a pilot when the charge was fired. How many Gs could be withstood without suffering severe injuries, particularly to the spine? On 24 January 1945 Bernard Lynch, an experimental fitter, volunteered to be shot up the seat rig in a succession of tests, each to a greater height. Close to ten feet he experienced considerable pain. Later tests imposed spinal damage. A rate of change of

Avro Vulcan c. 1960: fighter type control columns and WWII type instruments and panel layout. There are ejection seats for the two pilots but not for the other crew members. (Rolls-Royce)

109

acceleration as high as 250G/sec gives the spine a severe shock. However if the subject's spine was kept naturally erect with the vertebrae square to each other it could better withstand the sudden acceleration. The Defiant was replaced as a test vehicle by a Meteor Mk 3 so that the effects of ejection at speeds of 400 knots and higher could be assessed.

An important milestone in the history of the aircraft cockpit was set in place on 24 July 1946 when Bernard Lynch ejected at 280 knots at 8,000 feet from a two-seat Meteor. Another milestone in cockpit safety was the first live ejection using the Martin-Baker rocket-powered seat. In March 1962 Squadron Leader Peter Howard [later Commandant of the RAF Institute of Medicine] ejected from a Meteor flying at 250 knots but only 250 feet from the ground. Previously aircrew had been killed attempting to eject at a height too low to give time for the parachute to deploy. It has to be remembered that account has to be taken of the rate at which the aircraft is descending at the moment of ejection because the seat is also initially moving at the same speed. This adds to the problem. Since that date the ejection seat has been an essential part of the fighter/attack cockpit. James Martin's undoubted design leadership in the 1940s contributed to the saving of hundreds of lives every year. With only a few seconds in which to decide to eject, pull the firing loop and for the seat to be shot clear and the parachute fully open when flying close to the ground there was no time left in which to release the cockpit canopy. Therefore detonating cord is positioned on the inside of the canopy which fractures it to allow the seat and occupant to penetrate it as they move upwards.

An interesting decision relating to the provision of ejection seats was taken during the design of the Victor and Vulcan bombers for the RAF. Ejection seats were provided for the two pilots but not for the other aircrew. Traditionally the pilot or pilots have remained at the controls in the event of trouble in order to give time for the crew to bail out. Regrettably when the two V bombers were designed the configuration of the cockpit and adjacent crew compartment did not permit the installation of ejection seats for other than the pilots. After the Vulcan had been in service a few

years Martin-Baker designed a modification which would provide ejection seats for the crew 'in the back'. But this was not applied because of the cost. The excuse was that the Vulcans were to be taken out of service. However, they were not phased out for another ten years or more.

An ex-Vulcan Navigation Radar officer[6] describes the drill for making a successful escape. The two outboard seats swivelled inwards and, if necessary, the occupants could use an inflatable assister cushion to counteract G force so that they could stand and then step down to face the exit door. The one in the middle position would push the seat back and struggle around the other seats to reach the door. The exit door would be forced open by pneumatic rams and held open against the airstream. The exit had to be done in an orderly slide down the door. However, if the undercarriage was down they would hit the nose-wheel leg. They were told that they could slide down and use the door struts to swing around the nosewheel. This difficult task had been demonstrated in a wind tunnel. It is not hard to imagine what happened on a number of occasions in the event of a sudden, unexpected, airframe or total engine failure.

Ejecting at high Mach numbers

Following the deaths of many aircrew trying to escape from trouble by ejecting at high Mach numbers, during which they sustained horrific injuries from wind blast and erosion and thermal injury, the USAF equipped the B-58 Hustler with an escape capsule for each of the three-man crew. These enabled the crew to operate in a 'shirt-sleeve' environment.[7] As, for example, with the B-58 Hustler and the B-1, the crew of the General Dynamics F-111 are provided with an escape capsule. This comprises the complete cockpit section of the fuselage plus an extension housing life-support equipment and homing rescue beacon UHF transmitter. Flotation bags are mounted fore and aft and, as with the parachute, are deployed automatically.

Improved and more information

Before covering developments in methods of displaying and conveying information to aircrew a

One of the first departures from the RAF Basic Six panel. This is the principal instrument panel in a Folland Gnat arranged around an integrated system of attitude and horizontal situation indicators.
(Smiths Industries)

few words about aviation electronic systems or avionics are needed. Avionics have revolutionised the aircraft cockpit and other control positions. As with most advances in aviation, avionics development has been a gradual process. However there are degrees of gradualness. Pointer-on-dial mechanical and electro-mechanical instrument development made steady progress from 1914 onward but not until the 1940s was there any marked increase in the speed of development. Eventually these types were overtaken by electronic systems. At first in the 1960s this was a slow process. One of the retarding factors was the reluctance on the part of pilots in particular to accept new concepts for the ways in which information should be presented. The new avionic

displays had to be clones of the existing non-electronic instruments so that pilots who had to fly different versions of the same aircraft were not faced with extra training or led into making mistakes.

For the first two decades of the military jet aircraft the cockpits were usually equipped with instruments whose design was only slightly advanced from that of 1945. In the 1950s avionic display units were often 'shoe-horned' into the cockpit; as in the F-86D. Not only had space to be found in the cockpit for the display units but space had to be found somewhere in the fuselage for the associated 'black boxes'. This was achieved either by crowding out other equipment or by 'stretching' the fuselage. An example of the latter solution is the Lockheed Shooting Star which had been designed before the advent of search and attack radar systems. The fifteen black boxes with which it was later equipped were equivalent in volume to ten large suitcases. Eventually instru-

F-4 Phantom. A book on cockpits would be incomplete without the pilot's place in one of the world's most outstanding and long-lived military aircraft. The attack radar display is under the gyro gunsight. This photograph emphasises the trend in the 1960s to crowd more and more weapon-aiming equipment against the windscreen so as to limit the pilot's forward view.
(McDonnell Douglas)

ment designers were encouraged to think up new ways of presenting information to the pilot.

Jet aircraft were not only becoming much faster than their 'prancing-piston' predecessors they were increasingly more versatile and therefore far more expensive. These expensive and sophisticated machines required better instruments and extensive avionics systems as well as the means to find and attack targets of all types. At the same time the opposition was acquiring the means to track and shoot down aircraft;

particularly if they were operated at low level.

Instrument designers concentrated on two areas. Firstly, improving the individual pointer-on-dial instruments so that they provided clear and unambiguous information under all lighting conditions from the darkest night to the extremely bright unfiltered sunlight at high altitudes. Secondly, and of great importance to the future, combining functions in one display. A good example of this is the attitude director instrument (ADI). However, there were limitations to the complexity and number of small electric motors and feed-back devices that could be packed into an instrument case. As it was some instruments were eight inches (200mm) from front to back. These took up valuable space behind an instrument panel. They were also expensive to service and repair. Above all the format of a display, that

Below: *An electronic display of the horizontal situation to complement that of the attitude director. At the instant shown the aircraft heading is 010 degrees and a radio beacon has been selected which is at 067 degrees and 5.8 nautical miles away.* (Smiths Industries)

Above: *Rockwell B-1 bomber flight deck. Vertical scale instruments predominate and in this early 1970s giant bomber there are few electronic displays. The two pilots and the other two crewmen are contained in an escape capsule which can be fired clear of the fuselage.* (via Smiths Industries Archives)

is the alphanumerics and the symbols, could not be changed easily or quickly, and definitely not in flight. If for no other reason electronic displays needed to be invented.

The CRT of course had arrived in the cockpit in the early 1940s in the shape of AI, ASV radars and other electronic aids to navigation and target finding, such as Gee and H2S. Some German AI displays in 1945 even had colour to discriminate between different types of the information. By the end of WWII the CRT was a common feature of the fighting cockpit. However, it sat alongside the conventional pointer-on-dial instruments and remained for many years the only representative

Above: *Despite the size of the Nimrod maritime patrol aircraft of the RAF the cockpit is comparatively narrow. The 1997 version of this aircraft has electronic displays in place of the numerous pointer-on-dial instruments shown here.*
(Smiths Industries)

Left: *Navigation and systems control stations in an RAF Nimrod. Virtually an airborne office with every one 'head down' at their electronic interface.*
(Smiths Industries)

of the revolution in avionics which would eventually burst on to the scene in a proliferation of alphanumerics, symbols, maps, weather and other data; at first in monochrome and then in full colour. By 1980 the 'all singing, all-dancing' electronic displays in 'glorious Technicolor' were available to those air forces that could afford them.

In 1954 the USN published its thoughts on the cockpit of the future. The projected design featured one large combined information and weapon-aiming electronic display mounted above a 'desk-top' control panel which included a side-stick primary flight control. Although it expressed the navy's desire to improve the total cockpit interface it was in advance of the available avionic and display technologies. With the pilot's legs under the 'desk' the major part of the interface would have had to have been swung out of the way or ejected before the seat ejection sequence was triggered.

A bumpy ride

One requirement common to many specifications for tactical strike reconnaissance aircraft in the 1950s was the ability to penetrate enemy air space by flying at around 1,000 feet. At that height an aircraft flying close to Mach 1 was expected to be immune from radar detection. In the 1950s terrain-following electronics and other ground-avoidance devices were not available. The crew's task during a low-level penetration sortie was exacerbated by the effects of gusts, particularly over undulating territory. Gusts are the result of general choppiness and turbulence caused by obstructions at low level. Gusts not only increased airframe structural fatigue they also gave a bumpy ride for the crew. At times the crew would experience severe vibration through the seats. This was accepted to be one of the major crew fatigue problems of low-level penetration flying. In the UK research into ways of alleviating these effects included the use of spring-mounted seats.

Electronic aiming

Within the overall technological advances of aviation in the early 1960s the electronic Head-Up Display (HUD) represents a key element which had a far reaching effect on the design of the fighter/attack aircraft cockpit. Up to about 1960 the most advanced method of aiming guns and missiles was the gyro-based lead and drop computing sight. This was a development of the gyro-sight of WWII and differed only in its detailed refinements. Just as in the early 1930s

An important item in the history of the military aircraft cockpit. This is one of the earliest Head-Up Displays (HUDs) and not much larger than the gyro gunsight it replaced.
(Smiths Industries)

when collimated optics were reflected off the windscreen of RAF fighters, scientists, encouraged by pilots, envisaged methods of projecting both aiming symbols and other information directly onto the windscreen glass in front of the pilot (see chapter 3). In WWII experiments were made whereby the gyro-sight used the windscreen as the reflecting surface. The immediate goal in the late 1940s was to use a CRT to display aiming symbology and reflect it off the windscreen glass. However a practicable HUD, within our present meaning, had to await the development of the airborne electronic analog computer.

From analog to digital computer

In the early 1960s the electronic HUD became a key element in the design of the cockpits of the Buccaneer and the Harrier. The former's HUD was developed by GEC Avionics and the latter's by Smiths Industries. It says much for the skills of the development scientists in the UK that they were able to perfect an acceptable analog-computer HUD and weapon-aiming system before the advent of the digital computer. Eventually, the analog computer systems for head-up and weapon-aiming displays were superseded by digital computers able to perform calculations at greater speed with greater versatility and reliability and lower cost.

The digital computer started to revolutionise cockpit equipment in the mid-1960s. It became the essential basis for a number of avionic systems, one of which was the HUD. The computer took information from a number of different sources, such as the air data system, aircraft attitude and heading and presented it in the pilot's forward line of sight. An air data system typically senses, measures, computes and transmits to other systems pressure altitude, outside air temperature, Mach number, Equivalent Air Speed (EAS), angle of attack (Alpha), yaw angle and dynamic pressure. Although the HUD looked like an improved version of the gyro gunsight it was far more than that.

Elements of a HUD

A HUD display unit consists of three principal elements: a CRT, the many lenses of the optical system and the combining glass or glasses. The HUD's computer can provide a wide range of symbology and alphanumerics from which the pilot can select those appropriate to a particular flight mode. However, the final information process is non-avionic because it is just an optical display. There is therefore a limit to the vertical and horizontal fields of view. In a typical 1960s generation refractive optics HUD these were typically 12° and 18°. Diffractive optics using holographic technology provided increased fields of view. A notable example is the GEC Avionics Lantirn (Low altitude navigational targeting infra-red for night) HUD used in the F-16.

No longer does the pilot have to scan a number of discrete instruments in order to build up a complete picture of what the aircraft is doing, where it is going and what is needed to be done in order to achieve a specific goal. Within reason the HUD system can be programmed to present a wide range of symbols and alphanumerics. Most importantly and like the multi-function electronic displays which came later, the pilot can select the display to match the immediate operating phase i.e en route cruise navigation, target search, target acquisition (ground or air) and attack. The HUD can display any of these at a touch of a button as well as provide a continuous indication at the sides of the display of aircraft angle of attack, altitude, vertical speed, Mach/airspeed and heading.

Impact on cockpit design

As mentioned, the HUD, like the ejection seat, required some re-thinking of the traditional shape and volume of the fighter cockpit. This is emphasised by the fact that not all the 1950s generation aircraft had room above the instrument panel and within the frame of the windscreen to accommodate a HUD. A notable example was the English Electric Lightning in which there was not enough room between the top of the instrument panel coaming and the sloping windscreen in which to fit the display unit of a HUD. From 1960 onwards cockpit design decisions over dimensions and volumes had to include three key elements: pilot, ejection seat and HUD. (In American literature, for some reason unrelated to the technology, the plural of 'head' is often used, so that we read of 'heads up display'.)

At this point the reader may find the following generalised description of what a HUD does and how it is used helpful when considering the fighter/attack cockpit interface as a whole.

Part of the HUD concept in the early 1960s was related to the poor visibility conditions which obtain for much of the time in Europe. The Harrier and Jaguar squadrons of the RAF, for example, were required, in the event of a Soviet advance westward to 'take-out' formations of tanks and bridges in the face of formidable surface-to-air-missiles. Attacks would have been at low level irrespective of the visibility conditions. In those circumstances a pilot had to fly 'head-up' in order to navigate and avoid obstacles.

Opposite: English Electric Lightning c. 1960. Horizontal 'tape' airspeed and Mach number above large electro-mechanical attitude and horizontal situation displays. Against the windscreen is the gyro gunsight. The shape of the nose forward of the instrument panel did not afford room for an electronic HUD. The attack radar display unit fits into the space to the right of the gunsight. To the left are the twin throttle levers and the lever for the air brakes.
(British Aerospace)

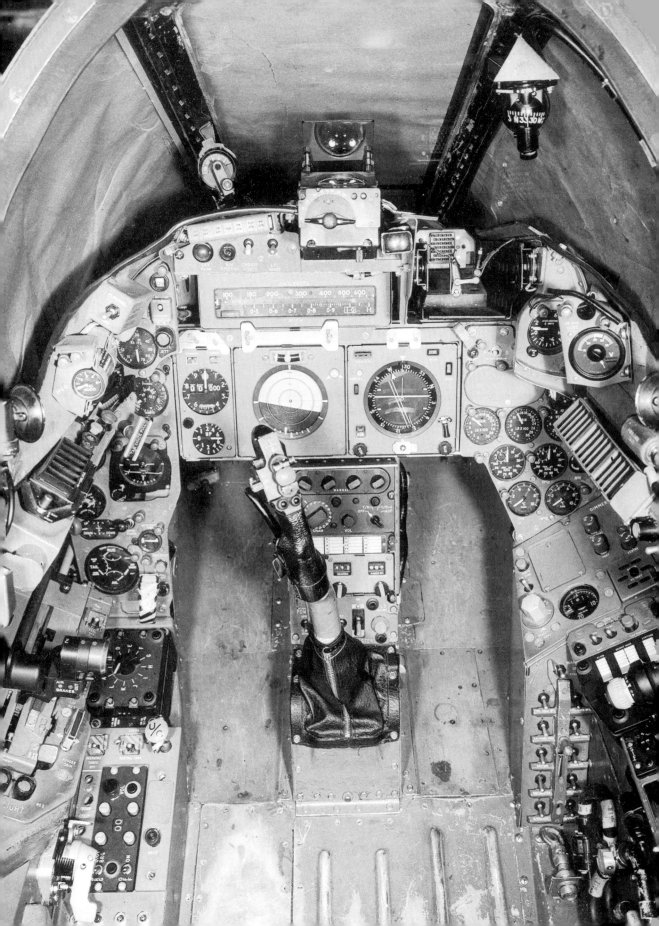

LTV Corsair II c. 1970. The cockpit, radome and air-intake are close together in the nose of the aircraft.

There was no time in which to refer to 'head-down' cockpit instruments. One of the disadvantages of the gyro sight, particularly in the ground-attack role, was the need for the pilot to fly a set manoeuvre when flying toward the target. The aircraft had to be flown smoothly and the speed kept within close limits. The inflexibility of this form of attack made the aircraft very vulnerable in the face of the enemy's defensive guns and missiles. In the 1950s there were significant improvements in the performance of anti-aircraft defences. 'Set-piece' attacks, with the aircraft flown to precise attack patterns, were no longer acceptable. For example, loitering close to a target in order to assess the best approach track cannot be indulged when the defences have sophisticated

fire-control systems. To avoid unacceptable attrition rates the pilot of a fighter/attack aircraft can afford to make only one pass at the target and that must be at high speed and as low as possible. Therefore the aiming system has to provide guidance of a high order and without too much delay. With the electronic HUD such attacks are made easier. However, even with a HUD the target has to be tracked smoothly and time allowed for the weapon-aiming computer to do its calculations.

Low-level attack is just one of the scenarios in which a HUD is essential. It can also be used for en route navigation and for air-to-air combat. When used in conjunction with an automatic navigational system the HUD presents the pilot with symbols and alphanumerics which are used to control the aircraft towards a selected en route waypoint or target. The moving map display is another avionic system which revolutionised the cockpit. The Ferranti COMED (Combined Map

A typical Head-Up Display (HUD) unit. This emphasises the designer's particular problem of finding room for avionic units in the forward space of the cockpit beneath the windscreen. (Smiths Industries)

Opposite: *Harrier GR Mk I cockpit of the 1960s in the decade before the move to wall-to-wall electronic displays replaced most of the 'clocks'. The HUD and the COMED were developed in parallel with the Harrier and were essential equipment to enable the pilot to make the most effective use of the aircraft's unique capabilities.*
(British Aerospace)

118

and Electronic Display) of the early 1970s did away with the need to take out the appropriate map from a number of maps, hold it on one knee, study it, fly the aircraft and avoid ground and enemy hazards.

An integrated HUD/navigation system can display a symbol on the combining glass in front of the pilot which is superimposed on a ground feature. For example if the pilot has time to look down at the moving map display to check the aircraft's position a ground feature previously selected would be marked. The same ground feature marker can be viewed head-up. It could be a bridge or bend in a river or some other topographical feature. Looking through the combining glass of the HUD the pilot is alerted by a flashing symbol. Without a HUD and in poor visibility the pilot may have a difficult problem in discriminating between the desired feature or target; particularly when in one second the aircraft has moved ahead almost another 1,000 feet. The reverse process, whereby the pilot visually identifies, unaided, a ground feature, is used to up-date the navigational system.

Although a HUD became an essential part of a fighter/attack aircraft as a weapon system this was at a price. Along with heavy non-distorting combining glass brackets, which produced blind spots, and the use of special reflective glass coating, which reduced the amount of light transmitted, the pilot's forward view was severely compromised in some aircraft of the 1960s and 70s generations.

This description of the HUD emphasises its range of abilities and the benefits it confers on the pilot. However, even though the HUD was greeted in the 1960s as the answer to the pilots' prayers, operational experience began to highlight some shortcomings; some of which could lead a pilot into a disaster. As John Farley[8], one-time chief test pilot responsible for Harrier development, points out, a pilot could become 'fixated' on the compelling display and be unaware that the alphanumerics and symbology were corrupted. He cites occasions when on a clear day the attitude symbology was not aligned with the real horizon. The problem of display errors in the early HUDs often arose because they were simplex, i.e. one channel, systems. Both the

aircraft's inertial reference system of gyros and accelerometers and the HUD electronics could produce errors. A pilot might have no idea that the display was corrupted; particularly as there was no monitoring system which could warn the pilot that there was disagreement between the HUD and the standby 'head-down' instruments. The problem could be exacerbated by inadequate electromechanical standby instruments. In addition, the freedom from roll and pitch limitations, compared with traditional flight instruments, given by the inertial reference sources encouraged pilots to attempt violent manoeuvres without visual references.

Early 1960s cockpit standards (SEPECAT Jaguar) to which have been added a GEC-Marconi COMED (Combined Map and Electronic Display) and a Smiths Industries HUD (Head-Up Display). The former provides a continuously moving 'map' type display with the aircraft position shown at the centre; the latter has had the typical HUD symbology highlighted. (Smiths Industries Archives)

This aspect of cockpit information displays is used to emphasise that throughout aircraft development over the past ninety-five or more years one new method of instrumentation, such as the HUD, cannot be considered or used in isolation of other instrumentation.

During the 1960s there was a gradual process of introducing more avionics into the cockpits of fighter/attack aircraft. The search and attack radar display units of the 1950s were usually 'squeezed in' by pushing some of the instruments to one side. However with the arrival of the electronic head-up display (HUD) a major change in both appearance and allocation of panel space had to be accommodated in cockpits whose basic dimensions and controls were not too different from those of WWII.

TSR2 c. 1964. Another example of instrument design lagging engine, airframe and aerodynamic technologies. The majority of the instruments are electromechanical. Had the TSR2 gone into production it is likely that by 1975 the cockpit interface would have been the subject of a comprehensive upgrade programme to take advantage of electronic displays matched to the latest sensor and weapon systems technologies.
(British Aerospace)

Integration

The Harrier is just one example of a cockpit whose design was basically based on principles and dimensions from an earlier time in aviation history. Not until the USMC took an interest in the aircraft and McDonnell Douglas assumed a large measure of responsibility for the design of the up-dated Harrier, the AV-8b, did the cockpit begin to match the demands of the air war of the 1980s. An era in which increasingly a pilot and his aircraft were becoming part of an integrated weapon-system in which the avionic systems dominated the control interface between the pilot and the global environment in which the aircraft operated was no longer limited to RT links. The search and attack radars were no longer the only extension of the pilot's range of unaided vision. RT air-to-air and air-to-ground was supported by data transfer links between ground and aircraft which gave the pilot large amounts of information.

Many of these changes to the avionic equipment and the many additional avionic systems required a completely new approach to cockpit design. Integration is an over worked word but it serves to describe a design philosophy which had to be adopted to an ever increasing degree in the 1970s. The then separate avionic systems, sensors and effectors had to be integrated. Had integration not taken place then cockpits would have become even more like the 'back of the clock maker's shop'. Pilots in particular would have become overwhelmed when trying to pay attention to too much information presented in many different and uncoordinated ways.

A number of well known aircraft types, particularly in the fighter/attack category, were the subject of upgrade programmes from the 1970s onward. One essential and first step was to sweep away the discrete 'clock' type electromechanical instruments wherever possible and replace them with multi-function electronic displays, such as CRTs. By using multi-function displays, from which the pilot is able to select particular sets of information, the overall quality of the visual interface in the cockpits was improved. These changes to the information and control interface were introduced in parallel with major upgrade programmes for all avionic systems with 'integration' the key word. The

Early version of the BAe Hawk with its typical 1960s trainer/attack cockpit. The different case sizes of the principal flight instruments precludes a symmetrical layout. However, as long as the information provided by the individual instruments is clear and unambiguous, design for the sake of design is of less importance.
(British Aerospace)

primary objective of the upgrade programmers was to allow air forces to improve the fighting potential of their existing fleet, reduce maintenance costs and delay the day when they were forced to take the, often expensive, step of going for new aircraft.

By the 1980s the general design approach for all types of military aircraft was one in which the cockpit and all aircraft systems, the majority of which had become avionic, was full integration.

Integration did not stop at the cockpit canopy and sides. It extended to the total operating environment with such systems as JTIDS (Joint Tactical Information Distribution System). This ensures that all weapon systems, aircraft, ground troops and ships in a theatre of operations are able to communicate and exchange tactical data over a common net.

Situation awareness (SA)

To some extent changes in the role of the human

Opposite: Cockpit of a Sea Harrier FA2. This shows the addition of two multi-function electronic display units flanking a central panel of electromechanical and barometric instruments. However there is no up-front control panel below the HUD, the controls for which are on the left side of the coaming.
(British Aerospace)

Saab J-35 F Draken cockpit with the Ericsson-Hughes interception radar scope occupying prime 'real estate' panel space. An example of target radar not integrated with the weapon sight.
(Saab AB)

pilot are related to the limitations of the human body; both physical and mental. The limits of human workload have had to be set against the need to maintain the pilot's SA. Workload has to be kept at an acceptable level. The pilot has to be kept fully aware of what is happening both inside the aircraft and outside as well as what will or may happen within the overall tactical situation when fighting a three-dimensional war: a war spread over millions of cubic metres of air space and possibly bounded on one side by the indistinct and confused picture presented by limited

visibility and the ground war. The importance of SA is examined in detail in chapter 6.

As mentioned, essentially it was no longer effective or safe to fly at tree-top height over undulating territory in low visibility looking for a target and attempting to aim at it while making frequent checks of instruments in order to navigate, avoid high ground, find and aim at the target. The term 'situational awareness' (SA) is appropriate for these conditions. Means, mostly electronic, have been progressively added since the 1960s to enhance a pilot's SA.

'Head-up' and 'eyes-out'

The period 1960–1975 saw a significant increase in the number and functions of electronic systems in all types of military aircraft. The new jet

General Description Vol 1
AJS37

07 Jun 1996

Chapter 1   Page 11

Saab AB
Saab Military Aircraft

Saab Vigen AJS37:
A complete guide to the cockpit.

MOTORSTOPP	PUMPNING	→ ONORMAL DRAGKRAFT
MTG, H <12	MINSKA ∝/n_z	FLYG MJUKT
ÄTERSTART 2 s	BEHALL GAS?	– MUNSTYCKSLÄGE –
BRÄ REGL MAN < 9	–överhastighetsAVBRYT	ÖPPET STÄNGI
–äl varv / lamp 20 s–	–ådön kvantsIe–	FALL LAST	FTG, H < 9
ORD START–STRÖMST	SLACK EBK		BRÄ REGL MAN (AUT)
FLYG MJUKT	HÖGSTA M VARV		MAX 570°
LÄNDA SNARAST	FLYG MJUKT		FÄLL VID BEHOV LAST
	LÄNDA SNARAST		LÄNDA? HOPPA?

(29)

16 START switch
17 TÄNDSYST switch (ignition)
18 LT–KRAN light (LP–fuel valve)
19 HUVUDSTRÖM switch (MASTER)
20 LT–KRAN switch (LP fuel valve)
21 Canopy handle
22 KB (ECM) switch
23 Light switch, left emergency checklist panel
24 ROLL CENTR roll trim indicator
25 Pitch trim indicator
26 IND LAMP HEL HALV switch (BRIGHT/DIM)
27 STRÅLKAST switch (landing/taxi lights)
28 NÖDBEL switch (emergency lights)
29 Emergency checklist panel
30 KONTR LAMPTABLA switch (lamp test)
31 Cabin pressure indicator
32 Brake accumulator pressure indicator
33 Left warning/caution panel
34 FR 22 control panel (radio)
35 Mission mode selector
36 Radar control panel
37 GENERATOR switch
38 Radar joystick
39 ÄTERSTART switch (engine restart) (obscured)
40 FR 24 control panel (radio)
41 LJUSRADAR light intensity knob (radar)
42 ALLMÄNBEL light intensity knob (floodlights)
43 PANELBEL light intensity knob (panel lights)
44 Landing gear handle
45 INSTR BEL light intensity knob (instrument lights)
46 Throttle friction
47 KABINLUFT GOLV handle (floor air) (obscured)
48 Landing gear handle emergency release
49 Aircraft technical log pocket (outside figure)
50 Arm restraining net
51 Holder for arm restraining net wire

1   Autopilot channel selector
2   NÖDTRIM ROLL switch (standby roll trim)
3   NÖDTRIM TIPP switch (standby pitch trim)
4   SIDTRIM switch (yaw trim)
5   FR test panel (radio)
6   EP–13 light– and contrast knobs
7   LJUDSTYRKA UK DÄMP knob (radio volume)
8   IR–RB FRAMSTEGN pushbutton (IR missile sequencing)
9   Yaw trim indicator
10 Air conditioning panel
11 RENFLYGN (balanced flight) knob
12 RB 24J seeker uncage button
13 NÖDSKJUT HUV pushbutton (emergency canopy release)
14 Throttle
15 KB (ECM) switch

Figure 6.   Saab AJS37 Cockpit – left side

Saab AB
Saab Military Aircraft
General Description Vol 1
AJS37
07 Jun 1996
Chapter 1
Page 12

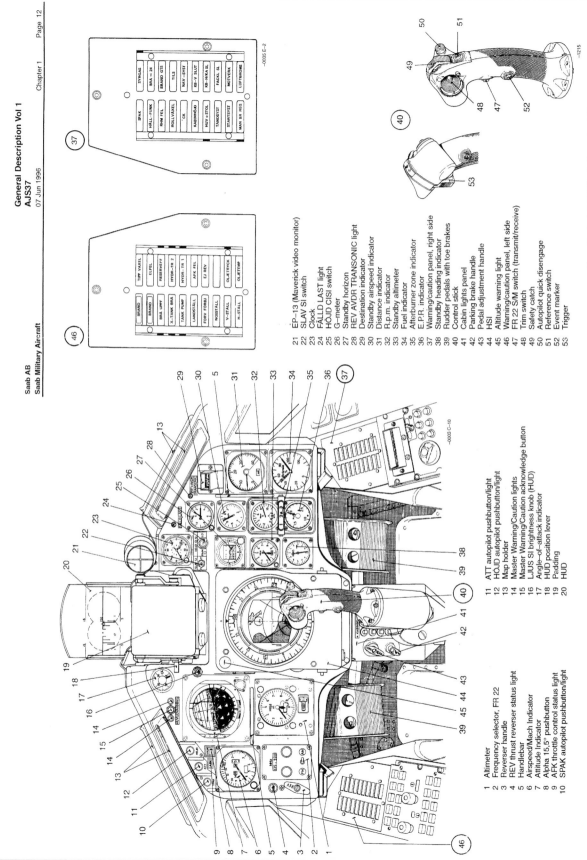

Figure 7.   Saab AJS37 Cockpit – center station

1   Altimeter
2   Frequency selector, FR 22
3   Reverser handle
4   REV thrust reverser status light
5   Handlebar
6   Airspeed/Mach Indicator
7   Attitude Indicator
8   Alpha 15.5° pushbutton
9   AFK throttle control status light
10 SPAK autopilot pushbutton/light
11 ATT autopilot pushbutton/light
12 HOJD autopilot pushbutton/light
13 Map holder
14 Master Warning/Caution lights
15 Master Warning/Caution acknowledge button
16 LJUS SI brightness knob (HUD)
17 Angle-of-attack indicator
18 HUD position lever
19 Padding
20 HUD

21 EP-13 (Maverick video monitor)
22 SLAV SI switch
23 Clock
24 FÄLLD LAST light
25 HOJD CISI switch
26 G-meter
27 Standby horizon
28 REV AVDR TRANSONIC light
29 Destination indicator
30 Standby airspeed indicator
31 Distance indicator
32 R.p.m. indicator
33 Standby altimeter
34 Fuel indicator
35 Afterburner zone indicator
36 E.P.R. indicator
37 Warning/caution panel, right side
38 Standby heading indicator
39 Rudder pedals with toe brakes
40 Control stick
41 Cabin lights panel
42 Parking brake handle
43 Pedal adjustment handle
44 HSI
45 Altitude warning light
46 Warning/caution panel, left side
47 FR 22 S/M switch (transmit/receive)
48 Trim switch
49 Safety catch
50 Autopilot quick disengage
51 Reference switch
52 Event marker
53 Trigger

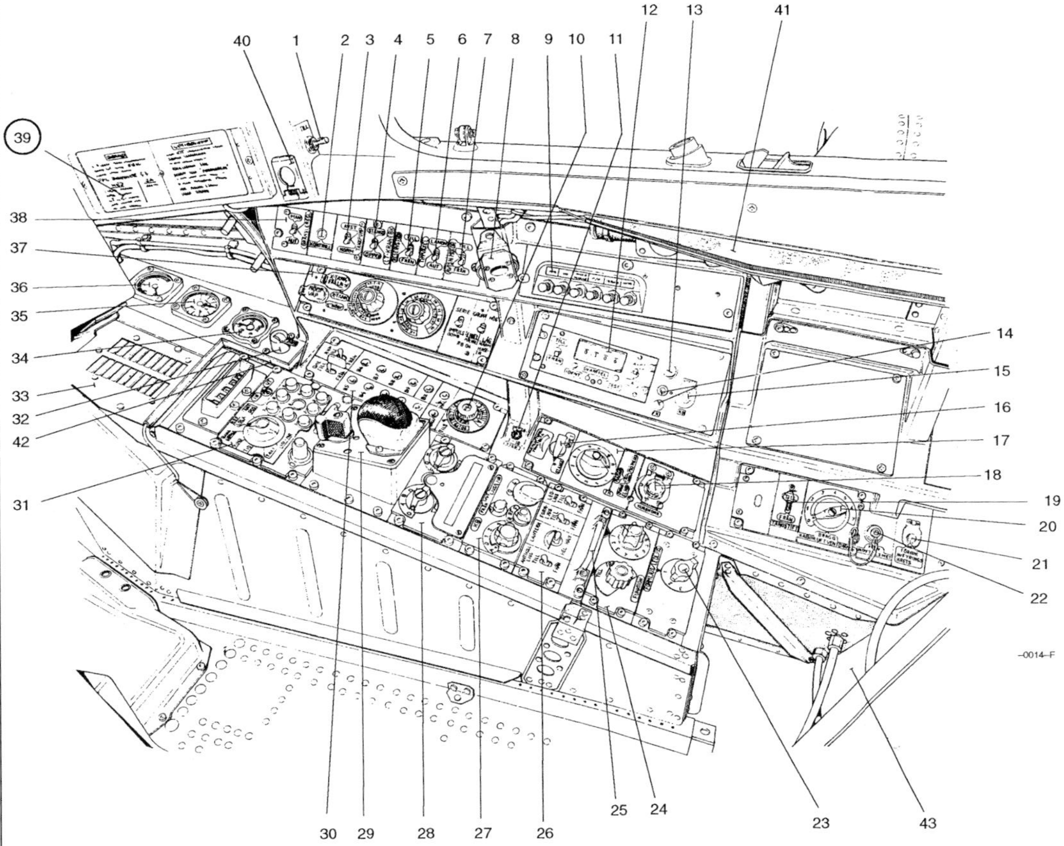

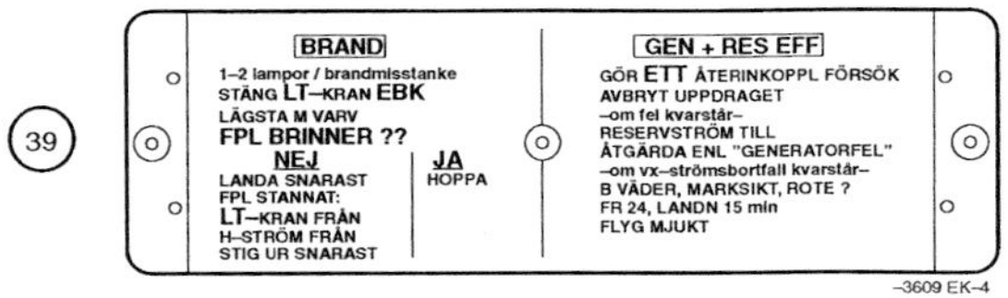

1 Light switch, right emergency checklist panel
2 KONTROLL test switch
3 TANKPUMP fuel pumps switch
4 LT-KRAN EBK LP fuel valve switch, afterburner
5 RESERVSTRÖM standby alternator switch
6 TIPPVÄXEL pitch gearing switch
7 AVISN MOTOR anti-icing switch
8 Central connection stowage
9 Circuit breaker panel
10 TILS channel selector
11 TILS channel group selector
12 SSR transponder panel
13 IFF light
14 FK functional test lights
15 KB weight-on-wheels bypass switch, ECM
16 VARMLUFTSPOLN FRONTRUTA windshield defogging knob
17 FK functional test control panel
18 KURSKORR heading adjustment knob
19 TÄNDSTIFT spark plugs switch
20 BRAGG KABINLUFT GPU cockpit cooling air control knob
21 FÖRBIK AVFYRINGSKRETS weight-on-wheels bypass switch, ECM
22 R.p.m. indicator test port
23 FORMLJUS/LEDLJUS formation lights intensity knob
24 IFF control panel
25 Handlebar
26 External lights panel
27 KB control panel (ECM)
28 KA control panel (ECM)
29 RB 05 missile controls
30 Nav panel
31 Data panel
32 Oxygen on/off switch
33 Warning/caution panel, right side
34 Oxygen pressure indicator
35 Exhaust Gas Temperature indicator
36 Nozzle position indicator
37 Weapons panel
38 BRÄNSLEREGL switch
39 Emergency checklist panel
40 Lens holder
41 Arm restraining net
42 Holder for arm restraining net wire
43 Protective mask box (outside figure)

Figure 8. Saab AJS37

engines alone required far more sophisticated methods of control and protection. There had to be a greater degree of automaticity and self-monitoring so that the pilot's only concern was that of one or two attention getting lights to indicate trouble or pending engine problems. Increasingly the aircraft was becoming an integrated weapon system and no longer a collection of disparate systems flying in formation. This trend added to changes in the look and function of both controls and instruments. It also enabled a greater use of 'head-up' and 'eyes-out' on the part of the pilot.

John Farley[9] recounts the comments of a fighter/attack pilot who was concentrating on aiming his missiles at a ground target. Just as he was about to press the 'fire' button he realised that two enemy aircraft were turning in on him. He had to change quickly from air-to-ground to air-to-air mode in order to defend himself. But the air-to-air mode was not immediately available until the attack on the bridge was completed. This highlights the need for an uncomplicated procedure for switching modes. This particular pilot was listened to by the design team for a new fighter with the result that the mission management system's four modes of operation could be easily selected by one switch on the throttle lever: 'up' and all systems go into air-to-air mode; 'down' for air-to-ground mode; 'centre' via 'up' for air intercept and 'centre via 'down' for navigation.

Who does what?

The relationship between the responsibilities of the human pilot and the avionic systems can be expressed in simple terms: the pilot manages the overall flight, selects the target and aims the aircraft and its offensive systems, such as missiles, towards the target: the avionics undertake the task of calculating and using highly accurate data to ensure that the target is hit at the first attempt. In other words the avionics fine tune and look after the small details. This leaves the pilot with the final say and the need to think and act in broad terms and therefore not necessarily in such precise terms as the avionic computers. When the balance between who does what is established satisfactorily then the pilot can use voice or touch

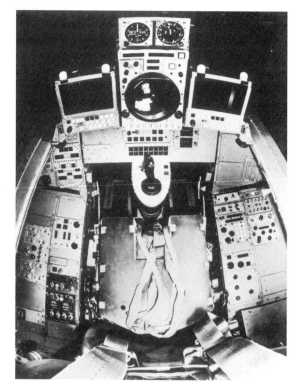

Aft cockpit of a Tornado. The number of controls and the large CRT displays emphasise the significant increase in avionic systems compared with earlier generation aircraft. The small control column is used by the navigator/weapon systems operator to select specific items on the tactical displays and to control the different weapons.
(British Aerospace)

inputs; such as 'Go to position XYZ: find and attack target type A using weapon system B'.

HOTAS and FADEC

Contributing to good SA in a fighter/attack aircraft is HOTAS (hands on throttle and stick) and the 'hands back' cockpit layout and equipment. The HOTAS concept recognises that in critical phases of flight, such as air-to-air combat or ground attack, a fighter/attack pilot cannot keep scanning 'head-down' instruments and looking and feeling for selector switches. The HUD and its up-front control panel, just below the combining glass, is a key element of HOTAS. Once the pilot has selected the required mode, such as ground attack, on the up-front controller panel there should be no need to take the hands

The pilot's display unit (PDU) of a head-up and weapon-aiming system. The substantial supporting structure for the two combining glasses, on which symbology and alphanumerics are projected, ensure that the optical system is not misaligned by high G loads.
(Smiths Industries)

off the throttle and stick. At the same time a full-authority engine control unit (FADEC) along with communications, utilities and stores (weapons) management systems relieve the pilot of any need to pay detailed attention to the displays of information or perform sequences of key, switch or lever selections.

Seeing the target

Irrespective of the type of aiming system, for guns, rockets, guided missiles or bombs monitored by human eyesight, the target has to be visible. Two vision enhancement techniques matured in the 1970s: Low Light Television (LLTV) and Forward Looking Infra-Red (FLIR). LLTV's ability is often demonstrated when domestic TV viewers are told that the game has been stopped because of poor light yet they can see right across the field. However LLTV has limitations particularly when the sensor is moved rapidly across a target. The preferred technique is IR and this is fitted to most of the world's first-line fighter/attack aircraft. It is important to note that IR cannot see through glass, water, earth and

rock. However it can 'see' through crystalline elements, such as germanium. Water vapour in the form of cloud and mist reduces the performance of a FLIR. Paradoxically it can 'see' through smog and smoke. This is because the atmosphere is made up of particles spaced well apart. LLTV and FLIR pictures can be presented on one of the electronic display units in the cockpit. At night a pilot can 'see' targets, otherwise invisible, by using a FLIR generated view displayed on the HUD.

Missile guidance

Much of what we call instrumentation in the fighter cockpit of the 1960s generation aircraft onward has been presented to the pilot in the form of attention and warning lights, annunciators and aural inputs. These provide an important part of situational awareness. In fighter/attack aircraft, lights and sounds as well as symbols on the HUD warn the pilot that the aircraft has, for example, flown into the coverage of a ground-based surveillance radar or is being tracked by a missile's target engagement system. When an aircraft is equipped with semi-active missiles the pilot has to keep the target within the aiming symbol on the HUD. This is a vulnerable time because violent manoeuvring to avoid enemy missiles cannot be used otherwise the radar beam along which the missile is 'riding' will be deflected away from the target.

As usual, advances in aviation technology provided an answer to the above problem. The Hughes Phoenix of the 1980s has an active target-seeking radar and is part of a 'fire-and forget' air-to-air missile system. Once the missile acquires the target it is on its own and the pilot of the launch aircraft is free to manoeuvre clear of opposing missiles.

TIALD

The Thermal Imaging Airborne Laser Designator (TIALD) system is just one example of the way in which avionics have improved the effectiveness of aircraft as weapon systems. The GEC-Marconi TIALD was developed in the early 1990s as a system which provides a target acquisition, identification and precision laser designator for laser-guided missiles and bombs. It can be used in

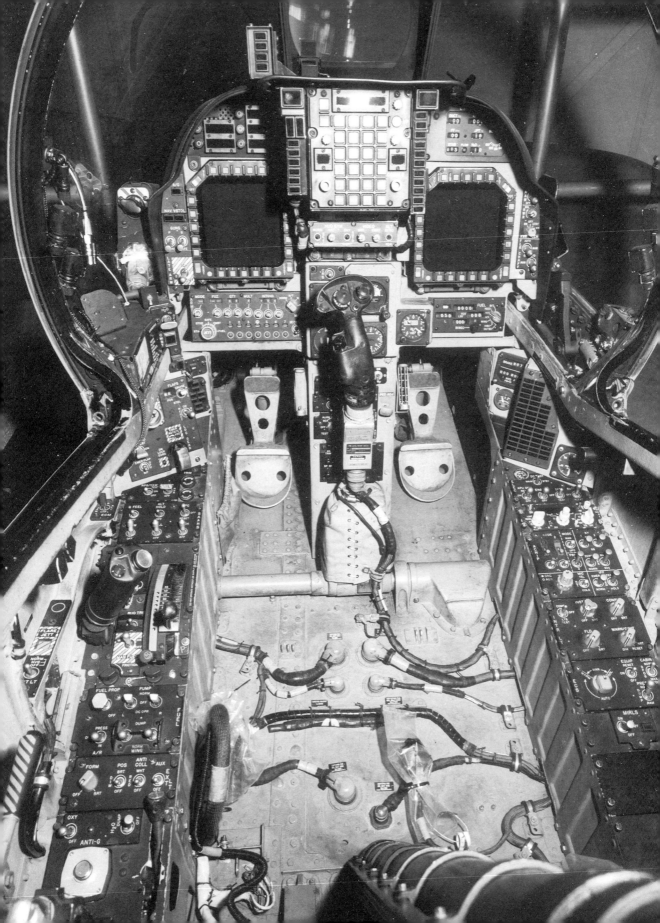

Workload is reduced by many avionic semi-automatic systems and by management systems. This is the selection panel for the missile management system in a Panavia Tornado. In older aircraft cockpits the pilot had to make time-consuming and complicated selection procedures using rows of switches. In the Tornado, the pilot with one touch can select Medium Range or Short Range air-to-air missiles or Gun. The weapons management system then arms the appropriate circuits and configures the aiming system to match the weapon characteristics.
(Smiths Industries)

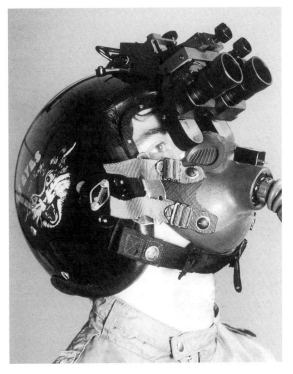

'Cat's Eyes' Night Vision Goggles (NVGs) which give the pilot the ability to see in the dark without affecting the scanning of the instrument panels. The NVGs enable the pilot to see FLIR images and the alphanumerics displayed on the HUD.
(GEC Avionics)

daylight or night and its effectiveness was demonstrated most convincingly in the 1991 Gulf War. The TIALD 'picture' can be presented on either the HUD or on a head-down display. In two-seat aircraft, display units are available in both cockpits. During the trials of the system it became apparent that there was the danger that the lone pilot in a single-seat fighter/attack aircraft might become 'fixated' by a head-down display and be unaware of the aircraft's attitude

Opposite: Harrier GR7. HOTAS and up-front control panel along with two large electronic multi-function displays improved the cockpit interface compared with that of the first version of the earlier Harrier.
(British Aerospace)

or trajectory. This potential hazard was overcome by providing aircraft attitude information on the TIALD display. TIALD is one of those systems which require an additional control column for use by the pilot or by both aircrew for 'steering' a laser beam onto a target.

Night vision

A typical NVG (Night Vision Goggles) unit usually presents a natural, that is unmagnified, view of the world. The light captured by the NVG's system of lenses and image intensifier is multiplied millions of times. They can construct a visible picture of the world in 'pitch black' lighting conditions. When NVG was first tried pilots found that they could not scan the cockpit instruments unless special cockpit lighting was used because normal instrument lighting, even dimmed to its lowest level, appeared so bright they were blinded by the glare. Because an NVG is focused at infinity it cannot be used to scan the head down instruments. Another problem, for the same reason, was the incompatibility of NVG with the HUD. NVG also limited the wearer's peripheral vision; however it could be used to scan a wide arc. Some NVG units could be automatically discarded as part of the ejection seat sequence. Modern NVGs enable the pilot to scan the night scene outside the cockpit and combine what is seen with the HUD. An example is the GEC Avionics Cat's Eyes NVG worn by USN and USMC pilots during night attack sorties. A particular advantage of these NVGs is that the wearer can alternate between the image intensified view outside the aircraft and the HUD. Helmet mounted displays (HMDs) are being developed which combine NVGs with target marking.

Touch screens

On the subject of the selection of display modes and information the CRT and the LCD can incorporate a touch screen interface. This enables the user to touch symbols, icons and alphanumerics displayed in order to activate or select a function. However, there are limitations to the user's ability to make a correct 'touch' when under stress, high G and vibration. Like DVI (Direct Voice Input), touch control may be limited to non-violent phases of flight. The trade offs among DVI, touch and HOTAS interfaces suggest that, although all three methods can be used, each is more appropriate to one particular phase of a flight.

Helmet-Mounted Displays (HMD)

The HUD is about to be superseded by the Helmet-Mounted Display (HMD). Among the reasons for this are the limited field of view and the need for the pilot to keep looking directly forward when using the HUD. The HMD uses the same electronically generated information but instead of projecting it onto the combining glass of a HUD the alphanumerics and symbology are projected onto and reflected into the pilots eyes by an optical system which is integral with the helmet visor. The advantage of the HMD is its much wider field of view in that it allows the pilot

to look in any direction and see display symbology wherever he or she looks. The wearer is not limited to looking straight ahead. An example of the HMD's versatility is when a target is spotted, be it on the ground or in the air, or to one side of the aircraft's track the aircraft does not have to be immediately pointed at the target as with a HUD. The aiming circle of the HMD is 'laid' over the target and the pilot presses the 'mark' button on the control column or, using DVI, says 'Mark'. The weapon-aiming system then knows the location of the target and uses that data as a basis for all subsequent attack calculations.

The HMD is another example of a common trend since the development of electronic displays whereby more and more information in the form of symbols and alphanumerics is added to the basic concept as experience is gained. Whether this trend is advantageous or counterproductive has yet to be determined. In the UK in the 1980s the Royal Aircraft Establishment (now the more

Viper II binocular Helmet-Mounted Display (HMD). (GEC-Marconi)

prosaic titled Defence Evaluation & Research Agency) determined from experiments that a Helmet-Mounted Sight (HMS) improved a pilot's target hitting score significantly. The 'kill' success, using simulated missile attacks rose from 35% using a HUD to 50% with a helmet sight. The aiming symbology included a circle to show the capture zone of the missile's seeker head, a letter 'C' to indicate that the seeker head was within the boresight of the HMS and a red dot which appeared if the missile was being steered too far away from the successful engagement axis.

The pilot taking part in the evaluation trials at the RAE liked the simple helmet sight but, as so often happens, they started to ask for additional information to be displayed; such as barometric height and angle of attack; thus expanding the HMS into a full HMD. And so the HMD, like the HUD before it, became the primary interface element in the cockpit.

The computer cockpit

In the decades of the 1980s and 90s more and more avionic 'black' boxes were added as the demand grew for aircraft able: to operate in all visibility conditions; to avoid, or be 'transparent' to, hostile electronics, such as radar and infra red radiation; to carry, aim and launch a number of different weapons; to refuel in flight; and, just as important as the other criteria, have a high degree of availability, flexibility, survivability, self-healing and ability to test themselves (built-in test). Another contributor to the growth of avionics is the requirement to provide an aircraft's crew with a comprehensive system of communications with a number of different ground agencies and with other aircraft. In 1940 an RAF or *Luftwaffe*

The 'Big Screen' at one of the anti-submarine operator's stations in an RAF Nimrod.
(GEC Avionics)

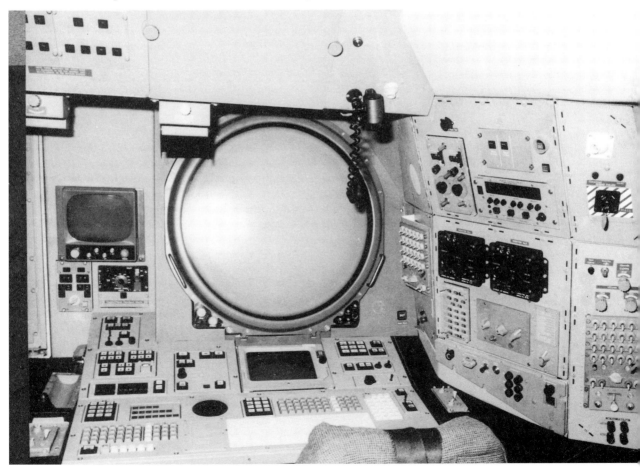

The massive size of the C-5 Galaxy USAF transport provides
room for a spacious cockpit. Note that many of the instruments
are of the vertical scale type.
(Falcon Aviation/PJC)

fighter pilot had only three or four different radio channels available for communicating with the ground and with others in the formation.

Increasingly the cockpit of single and tandem seat aircraft became the 'systems manager' station as direct control of many aircraft functions were given over to computer based systems. With the increases in available information in the cockpit and fully automatic aircraft systems, aircrew have become decision makers rather than searchers for information. Although whenever it comes to the crunch the human pilot is still the best and most powerful, in terms of option-taking, of all the computers on board the aircraft.

Multi-function throttle levers

In the beginning the throttle was little more than a simple lever. We have seen how over the decades

of military aviation development the throttle lever has acquired more and more switches and buttons. The first examples were the water injection system selector switch and the twist grip for the stadiametric ranging input to the gyro gunsight. Intercom and radio, press-to-talk (PTT), buttons followed. Today, the throttle levers of the Eurofighter can have as many as twelve switches and buttons.

Thrust and geometry control

The Yak-36 Forger and the Harrier were the only fixed-wing fighter/attack aircraft to enter squadron service in the 20th century as successful short take-off and vertical landing (STOVL) types. The thrust controls in the Harrier included an additional control lever for rotating the four engine exhaust nozzles. The lever is moved back to rotate the nozzles: downward for short take-offs, for hovering flight and forward for VIFF (Vectoring In Forward Flight).

The variable geometry F-111 also required a 'third' lever for selecting the sweep angle of the wings. This raised the question: which way should it move? In the Harrier the pilot rotates the nozzles downward by moving the lever back. In the F-111 the lever is moved forward to sweep the wings back for high speed flight. This is, of course, contrary to basic ergonomic thinking that a lever should move in the same direction or sense as the system it is controlling. Therefore the lever should have moved back to effect greater wing sweep. However General Dynamics decided that the lever should move forward in the same direction as throttle movement for high speed flight. The same reasoning was applied to the relationship between the Harrier's nozzle lever and speed.

The Panavia Tornado's wing sweep mechanism is controlled automatically by a configuration computer. This controls wing sweep, flap and slat settings so as to to keep down pilot workload during air-to-air combat. In addition to thrust, primary flight control and variable geometry control levers some aircraft have another hand lever for 'steering' the weapons system, such as a laser, onto a target.

By the time the F-16 arrived the number of controls and selectors distributed between the throttle and the control column had increased to as many as eleven. In the F-16 the throttle lever controls included radio transmit, ranging selector, antenna elevation, head-up display cursor and speed brake selector. The side-mounted stick carried the controls for trim, weapon release, designate/return to search, NWS/ARDISC/MSL, step and camera/gun trigger. As Gunston and Spick pointed out[10] 'Just how far we can go in interfacing perhaps 20 or 30 systems through two hand controllers is something we have to find out. After a certain level of complexity is reached the HOTAS idea probably becomes self-defeating.'

In addition to a seat angle of 30 degrees and a side-stick the F-16 has one of the first combined windscreen and canopy transparencies. By dispensing with the normal windscreen frames the pilot's forward view is virtually unobstructed. However there is a price to be paid because the whole of the canopy has to be as thick as the forward section and is therefore heavier than the usual arrangement of separate canopy and windscreen. The penalty does not stop there because the canopy is too thick to be fractured as

part of the ejection sequence. Therefore it has to be jettisoned first. A side-stick and an ejection seat inclined back by 30 degrees are also features of Taiwan's indigenous fighter the Ching Kuo.

The span of technological advances

In the last two decades of the 20th century the pace of technological advance, particularly in avionics, increased significantly over that of the 1960s and 70s. An example is the cockpit and its equipment in the McDonnell Douglas F-15E. In the mid-1970s its predecessor the F-15A had what one writer called 'plethora of knobs and dials'. There was only one CRT and this occupied a secondary location in the cockpit's real estate.

The cockpit of the F-15A reflected the standards of the 1970s. Apart from the HUD and the horizontal situation indicator, it was not all that different from the cockpits of WWII. The HUD was the only electronic display. The rest of the instrumentation consisted of pointer-on-dial indicators and warning and attention lights. Compared with the A version the F-15E provides a very different operating environment for the pilot. The panel of 10 or 15 'clock' type instruments of the early generation of F-15s has been replaced by electronic multi-function displays. The HUD and its up-front control panel and the numerous selector switches and buttons of the electronic and electrical systems take up most of the panel space in front of the pilot. Flat-panel electronic displays are 'wall-to-wall'. This cockpit along with that of the F-18 exemplify the advances made over fifteen years in avionics as applied to the aircraft control interface and is an example of the ever steepening curve of avionic systems growth.

Side-stick

The Wright brothers adopted 'side-stick' control as did some of the other aviation pioneers. But by the end of WWI the control column set between the pilot's knees had been established as the standard arrangement. In WWII the 'side-stick' control, as we now know it, made a tentative appearance in some B-24s as means of directly commanding the autopilot. In the Soviet Tu 16 jet bomber and in its civil version (Tu 104) a side-

135

stick type autopilot control was mounted on the right-hand arm rest of the captain's seat.

The side-stick idea was revived on and off in the 1950s[11] but with the need to connect the primary flight control directly through mechanical linkages to the ailerons and elevator, even if power-assisted, there was not enough room at the side of the pilot for the required side to side movement. The side-stick only became practicable when fully powered controls and 'fly-by-wire' system, with no mechanical reversion in the event of failure, were developed.

Placing the principal control for roll and pitch to one side has both advantages and disadvantages. Placed to one side it no longer obscures the instruments and controls in front of the pilot. One disadvantage might seem to arise should the pilot lose the use of the right-arm and hand. However if that were to happen then there might be no alternative to ejecting because the modern cockpit requires both hands on the controls for most of the time. In any event, if the pilot is injured it is also likely that the aircraft is damaged and therefore has to be abandoned.[12] During a survey of pilots' opinions on the subject the majority favoured the conventional 'centre-stick' because of the real or subjective protection it afforded to vital parts of their anatomy.

The cockpit of the EF2000 Eurofighter was designed to have the control column in the conventional centre position. As the aircraft is flown by a fly-by-wire system then a side-stick could have been used. One of the reasons for not going to a side-stick was the need to retain standardisation with other NATO aircraft. The F-16 was designed around 'fly-by-wire' from the start. This allowed the use of a side-stick control which in turn provided room for a semi-reclining posture for the pilot to offset the effects of high G but, so it is reported, accompanied by neck ache.

The side-stick has been and continues to be the subject of controversy. It is not only its position and accessibility to the right-hand only, that originally caused much debate but the use of 'force' rather than movement to effect control. The pressure exerted by the F-16 pilot's hand is sensed by force detectors built into the stick, rather in the manner of strain gauges. In the prototype, the YF-16, the stick was rigid but after

flight trials it was agreed that the stick be given a small amount of movement. An example of limited movement is the joystick used with computer flight simulation games.

Prone or supine?

The proposals to have a prone or supine position for the pilot which have been put forward from time to time have usually had one major drawback. This is the difficulty of effecting control movements using the hands and arms; particularly in the years before fly-by-wire with small hand controls was developed. Both the prone and supine positions require supports to prevent severe neck ache on a long flight.

In a version of the F-7F Tigercat (1952) a supine pilot's position was tried. The seat angle could be varied between nearly upright to right back. In the supine position the pilot experienced an odd sensation when going feet first during the inverted phases of a loop. The objectives of the design were to give the pilot an upright position for take-off and landing, a semi-reclining anti-G angle for combat and fully reclined for long-range cruise.

The Sukhoi 37 of 1996 demonstrated both the 'Cobra' and the 'Somersault' manoeuvres. In the latter the aircraft climbed vertically and came to a stop literally standing on its tail. The pilot then allowed it to fall backwards so as to rotate 180 degrees about its transverse axis before diving away. The pilot experienced the full range of seat positions. Throughout the manoeuvre the pilot, although well ahead of the aircraft's CG, was not subjected to any significant G effect; unlike a loop in which the pilot is subjected to positive G.

Before the STOVL technique, using vectored jet thrust, was perfected attempts were made to achieve absolute vertical take-off by providing pro-

Opposite above and below:
In an attempt to mitigate the adverse effects of high G forces a number of prone-pilot cockpits were tried during the 1950s. This is a modified Meteor.

The line drawing shows how in an emergency the pilot's 'couch' could be released at the aft end and allowed to swing downward so that he could drop below the aircraft.
(Aeroplane Monthly)

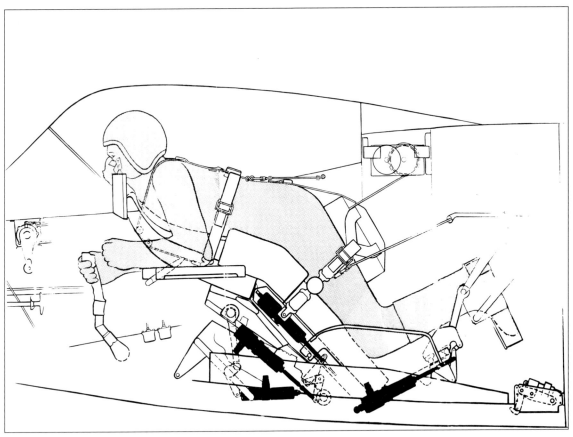

peller thrust in excess of the aircraft's weight. An example is the Convair XFY-1. This was an experimental single-seat fighter for testing the viability of operating a tail-sitting, vertical take-off and landing aircraft from ships. The pilot's ejection seat was mounted on hinges so that it could be tilted toward the instrument panel during vertical flight.

In Britain in the 1950s there was a prone-pilot research programme using a Meteor. The pilot lay prone in an attitude similar to that of Leonardo da Vinci's proposed man-powered flying machine. As with many unusual positions proposed, abandoning the 'prone' Meteor was a complicated affair. In the event of trouble the pilot had to release the up-locks of the couch on which he lay. This allowed it to swing down around the forward-mounted hinges. The pilot was then able to undo his harness and descend by parachute. Of course when trouble occurs in a high-performance aircraft the time available in which to get clear is often less than it takes to read the last three sentences. A prone-pilot position and controls were also evaluated in the Reid & Sigrist Bobsleigh.

Face forward?

Usually pilots are seated facing forward. There have been exceptions of which the special Vickers Victoria used by the precursor of the RAF Institute of Medicine is an example. For research purposes a pilot's seat with controls and instruments was installed in the fuselage facing aft and with no windows. The object was to study a pilot's response to sensations of aircraft movement when attempting to maintain control using instruments only. Eventually the development of realistic flight simulators also made it possible to study a pilot's ability to fly blind and to recover from violent manoeuvres if necessary when facing aft.

Notes

1 Champanis, A. (1965) *Research Techniques in Human Engineering*, p. 61. Johns Hopkins.
2. O'Rourke, G.G. (1966) *Proceedings of US Navy Institute*, p. 123. US Navy Institute Press.
3. Price, A. (1965) *The Spitfire Story*, p. 151. Arms & Armour.
4. Robinson, D.H. (1973) *The Dangerous Sky*, p. 214. Foulis
5. Lovesey, Prof. *Applied Ergonomics* Sept. 95 edn., p. 139.
6. Fox, N.H. Correspondence with the author.
7. Robinson, op cit., p. 242.
8. Farley, J.F. Correspondence with the author.
9. Ibid.
10. Gunston & Spick (1983) *Modern Air Combat*, p. 74. Salamander.
11. Coombs, L.F.E. (1959) Getting to Grips with the Stick; *Flight* 27 Feb. edn. p. 284.
12. Coombs, L.F.E. (1987) TriStar Today, Tornado Tomorrow: *Flight International* 3/10 Jan edn. p. 29.

The alternative to 'clock' type instrument presentation. This is for a four-engine aircraft. Although the presentation of details is clear and compressed, compared with individual 'clock' type displays, it has been criticised because of the possibility of the readings for one engine being confused with another.

CHAPTER SIX

DESIGNING THE COCKPIT

The simple aircraft is dead, and so is the simple cockpit.[1]

Introduction

Control and information interfaces are all around us, whatever our activity. Whenever we need to travel, to communicate, to make war or to help others there has to be a control and information interface to enable us to interact with the machine world.

Throughout history humans have devised ever more complex machines with which to perform tasks outside the limits of their innate ability. Some of the tasks, particularly those of pre-history, have been directed at food production; including irrigation and manipulation of the earth's surface materials. Some tasks have been concerned with transport, for both pacific and belligerent purposes. Others have been part of exploration and some just part of natural curios-ity.

Each type of machine or mechanical artefact, be it primitive plough or moon-landing vehicle, has had to have some form of control and information interface. The interface can be conveniently thought of as having three contigu-ous elements or surfaces: the machine; the controls and instruments; the human operator.

Although the 'instrumental' element may seem out of place in ploughing with animal power nevertheless throughout history ploughmen or ploughwomen have received information through their hands as to the way in which the plough was performing. Their eyes provided an 'instrumental' view based on the view ahead. At the end of each furrow the horse or ox had to be turned on the headland. This required a set of controls, namely the reins. Therefore the control and information interface of the plough was just as important to the human operator as the interface is to the modern aircraft pilot: except that the pilot is in control of a machine capable of moving at 1,000 feet per second (300 m per second) and having to make critical control decisions within a second.

Of all the interfaces, that of the aircraft has presented and continues to present some of the greatest challenges to designers, human factors people and aircrew. Of course in the first decade of powered heavier-than-air flight the pioneer designer/aviators had no reference books from which they could obtain design guidance. They were very much on their own and venturing not only into the unknown aspects of flight but also into uncharted ways of arranging controls and providing instruments to improve both the efficiency and safety of flight.

Before dealing with some of the problems and solutions of cockpit design at the end of this century some words on the human sense organs are needed. These are the organs used to determine what is happening and what may happen. They are included as an introduction because the human pilot is the most important programmed and re-programmable computer in an aircraft. The pilot provides a sensor and control interface between aircraft systems and between the aircraft and the world outside.

The human computer uses aural, visual and movement sensors and provides effectors which initiate control actions by using head and eye movement and finger, hand and foot actions. Other sensors are used to detect changes in the environment such as temperature and humidity. Of all the sensors, the visual is most important and represents constraints and requirements on the cockpit designer. Visual sensing of the real world and of the artificial world of instruments and electronic displays is not just a matter of looking. Seeing something is not necessarily the same thing as perception. For example, a branch of psychology, Gestalt, suggests that if a number of aircraft are seen at a distance and they are known to be hostile then the number perceived is likely to be higher than the actual number.

Another aspect of seeing relates to perceiving the expected and not the actual. This is a common human failing. On occasions many of us act on a first glance and assume, which is part of perception, that what we were expecting to see is actually there. An extreme example is the transport aircraft pilot making an instrument approach in low visibility who assumes that the rows of lights ahead mark the runway whereas they are the highway lights to one side and parallel to the runway. Another example is the fighter/attack pilot who sees a group of armoured vehicles and launches missiles at it and scores a 'blue on blue', because that is where he expected to find the target and the unfortunate friendly vehicles looked like the expected target.

From our earliest years we learn to react to moving objects and to the apparent relative movements among objects which make up our view of the world. We quickly learn that some actions are better than others whenever we react to the real world. With experience we learn the most effective actions and we react in the same way in future encounters when perceptual inputs are received.

Occasionally the real world does not appear or change in expected ways and then we may become confused, frightened or disoriented and react incorrectly. The result of this can be errors on the part of a pilot. To avoid errors or to reduce their adverse effects careful attention must be paid to the detail design of instruments and controls.

Within the overall subject of perception in and from the cockpit a distinction has to be made between the way in which a pilot visually perceives the real world and the artificial world of instrument displays. The pilot's view of the world outside the cockpit is made up of familiar shapes, colours and relationships. Sometimes these elements are unfamiliar or confused because of obscuration or distortion by the atmosphere and light level.

When all or some of the elements of the real world are hidden by others, or by insufficient visibility, pilots expect them to appear eventually. As mentioned, this reliance on expectation can have disastrous consequences if based on false or insufficient clues.

The importance of visual perception or rather the correct interpretation of perceptual inputs, is particularly applicable to the pilot's control and judgmental tasks whenever using simultaneously real world and artificial world information. Although, in the absence of visual enhancement systems, the two are not used simultaneously, except when combined in a HUD or HMD for example, because the pilot alternates between the 'inside' and the 'outside' views. Nevertheless each time the source of information is changed the pilot has to adjust quickly to different visual tasks. These include adapting in milliseconds to changes which have occurred in the real world and in the artificial world presented by the cockpit instruments since the last scan. For this reason and others, psychologists attempt to understand as much as possible about how the pilot sees and perceives the real world. This subject is also of great importance in relation to analogue and pictorial representations provided by instruments.

Perhaps the most important factor in human visual perception is our knowledge of the identity, characteristics and relationships among the objects and features of the world around us: for the pilot this is concentrated in the view ahead. During a critical phase of flight, such as a landing in poor visibility, the pilot has a mental image of the expected perspective shape of the runway. This image is primarily based on the visual experience of hundreds of previous landings and is triggered by a glimpse of only a small part of the view ahead and features on the ground. Moving objects and changes to the view ahead are more important to the pilot than the fixed relationships between objects ; although these are of some importance in that they form the ever changing perspective view of surface features when flying close to the ground during an air-to-ground attack or during the final stage of a landing.

Our knowledge of the world we perceive is our most valuable tool in interpreting instantaneous perceptual information and changes to that information; both subtle and gross. This knowledge usually enables us to react to the information quickly and correctly; but sometimes it does not.

Machine-interface-human

At one time in aviation history there were few human factors specialists. Cockpit design proceeded largely without the benefit of either pilot opinion or of human factors knowledge. Today we have the benefit of a vast fund of information about the ways in which the human pilot sees and perceives. We also know more about the way in which physical sensations and sound affect a pilot's performance. Pilot opinion based on 'hands-on' experience is an important input to the study and design of fighting aircraft cockpits; but in the past this valuable information input was often neglected.

With increasing aircraft performance, design became a protracted and expensive business. It became far removed from the time when, it was alleged, Tom Sopwith sketched the outline and principal features of his first aircraft on the hangar wall in chalk. However, even in those early years standard engineering design procedures in the shape of drawing office blueprints and stress calculations had to be applied before proceeding further. When it came to the cockpit and its equipment, the few available instruments, the basically simple stick and rudder bar and the engine controls did not pose any particularly difficult design decisions. As already mentioned, considerations of aircraft control and per-formance took precedence over cockpit design which, in turn, meant that the pilot and cockpit equipment were low in the list of task priorities.

In general military aircraft cockpits of the 1920s were not much different from those of the WWI. After 1930, when the research and develop-ment of 'blind' flying instruments and the inclu-sion of more electrical systems began to take effect in production aircraft, the cockpit became more crowded with instruments and controls. This reflected the significant increases in aircraft per-formance and versatility compared with those of WWI. However what had not advanced to any discernible degree was cockpit design related to improving the pilot's 'work station'; as some might call it. What we now term human factors and ergonomics were virtually unknown disciplines until the 1940s. Previously scientists concerned with people at work had concentrated on their overall performance; particularly fatigue, with little or no attention given to the way they reacted to the tools, such as instruments and controls, of their work station. Their health and

safety was usually the province of a separate group of researchers. In the UK, for example, their work was concerned primarily with the requirements of the Factories Act. A parallel study was that of Professor Gilbraith in the USA who introduced the science of time and motion study.

Among the scientific papers in the UK of the 1920s there are few related specifically to the aircraft cockpit and the pilot. Of 118 scientific papers and books covering human engineering listed in a 1959 publication only two covering cockpit factors were dated 1940 or earlier. These facts highlight the upsurge in human factors/ergonomic studies generated from after WWII by the rapid rise in technology, particularly in aviation. The war introduced new and complicated machines; none more so than the aircraft. Accidents and incidents in aviation became an accepted part of airforce life. Many were caused by straightforward mechanical failure because structures and engines were far more prone to failure than in later decades. Courts of inquiry tended to attribute accidents to 'pilot error'. Those inquiring into the cause of an incident or accident were rarely experienced in human factors. They tended to concentrate on reasons why the pilot had failed to benefit from experience on the aircraft type so as to avoid getting into what was generally accepted as an undesirable part of a particular aircraft's per-formance envelope, such as too tight a turn on the approach with flaps and undercarriage down inducing a stall; or pulling too much G at high speed similarly resulting in a different but equally unwanted stall.

Throughout the history of the aircraft cockpit the interface between man and machine has seldom been ideal. Both sides have been deficient in one or more aspects. The human element has well known physical limitations, particularly when removed from the normal 1,013mb at 15°C atmosphere or when exposed to excessive G forces. The machine element has limitations of which the most significant is that of inflexibility when compared with the human element and a tendency to embrace the laws of Sod and Murphy with enthusiasm.

A look back

Before considering the design of a cockpit for a new fighter/attack aircraft it is worthwhile looking back again at the evolution of the cockpit. But this time in relation to the information presented to the pilot.

In WWI the number one information source and sometimes the only one, was the human eyeball. A contact patrol over the Western Front took off and headed in the direction provided by the pre-flight briefing. Once airborne there was no way, since there was no RT, in which a change in the tactical situation could be conveyed from those on the ground to the formation leader. The formation depended for both its survival and for carrying out the sortie on visual clues from the ground. These may have been discerned easily or they may have been confused by the 'fog' of war. Similarly, anti-Zeppelin and anti-Gotha patrols over England were only as effective as the visual information link. Signals on the ground, flak bursts and co-operating searchlights were usually only effective in reasonable visibility. As mentioned in chapter 1, at the end of WWI a form of RT control was instituted and the night fighter pilots were no longer on their own.

Until the advent of radar, the control of interceptors depended largely on sound location and ground observation posts to provide information on the location and track of a hostile force. All this meant that fighter pilots of the 1930s still depended very much on a visual search once they had arrived at the position and height determined by the controller. A large error in the calculated position of the enemy might leave the interceptors searching a large volume of airspace and at the same time approaching the moment when they had to break off because they were at the limit of their operating range.

As mentioned in chapter 4, airborne interception radars significantly improved the chances of an interception, particularly at night. At the same time they introduced for the first time the problem of excessive crew workload because the 1940s radars required much adjusting and concentration to achieve a 'kill'. A night fighter crew had to keep a running mental picture of where they were and where the target was likely to be. In the night-fighter war in the second half of WWII we can

find examples of what we now know as lack of situation awareness, the concept introduced in chapter 5.

Situation awareness

From the 1950s onward more and more information was being provided to an aircrew. Instead of suffering, as the preceding generation had, a lack of information they were now being overloaded with electronically generated data. Each item of information on its own could be assimilated and acted upon. However when the data started to multiply, aircrew had to keep one step ahead of the situation both inside and outside the aircraft. Part of the situation awareness problem in the 1950s and 60s arose from inadequate methods of presenting radio, radar, weapon-aiming and aircraft systems status. It took over thirty years to develop information and management systems which reduced the incidents of aircrew misreading or misunderstanding information inputs. By the end of the three decades there was also a better understanding of the problems and solutions of situation awareness (SA).

Since the advent of utilities and communications management systems aircrew have been

The original BAe Hawk Trainer cockpit with electromechanical instruments.
(British Aerospace)

relieved of much of sub-systems management tasks. But having reduced pilot workload the designer must not treat that as a bonus and increase workload in other directions. Again we are back in the trade-off market. As noted, the cost of modern military aircraft often demands a multi-role capability, which, in turn, imposes the need for a wide range of systems. Both the designer and the air force, for different reasons, may want a single-seater. However, the one-pilot cockpit may finish up as the most advanced, the most sophisticated and the best equipped of its generation but at high cost and at the expense of high workload for the pilot.

Over the last ten years those concerned with the design of cockpits and the ways in which the human pilot thinks and reacts to events both inside and outside the cockpit have realised that the pilot must at all times be aware of all that is happening or is about to happen. The pilot's SA has to be kept at the highest level. To use a crude example: the pilot sees the ground target ahead; arms the weapon system and follows the commands of the aiming system. All is set to press the 'FIRE' button. Instant blackness and the aircraft and its pilot are destroyed. What happened? The answer is a complete lack of SA. The only thing with which the pilot was concerned was the target. He did not see the enemy missile batteries or hear the missile-warning note in his helmet.

Extending the previous example further: an attack aircraft pilot attempting to navigate to a target which is surrounded by high ground in poor visibility may not be fully aware of what is happening. Without adequate sensors, as well as ECM systems to warn him of and protect him from enemy threats, he is unlikely to succeed. As mentioned in chapter 5, fixating on the HUD and failing to realise that the display is corrupted can be fatal. Awareness of the complete situation outside and inside the cockpit is essential. Therefore the cockpit and its equipment must at all times ensure that the pilot is aware of what is happening and what will happen.

The primary design target, once the essential role functions of the aircraft have been met, is to provide a cockpit which affords the pilot maximum SA. Unless that design aim is achieved

no amount of sophisticated weaponry and aircraft agility and performance will guarantee superiority over the enemy. A lack of information can arise from a number of causes one of which is inadequate sensors and an insufficient view of the world outside the cockpit. Conversely, there may be sufficient sensors and view of the real world but the total information is presented in a confusing way.

The aircraft might be equipped with a most comprehensive range of avionic aids. The pilot might be presented with information on where the target is, how to get to it, what enemy defence systems have 'locked on' to the aircraft and the state of its major systems. The HUD might provide primary flight data, the target-seeking radar might display its information and the ECM display might indicate locations of surface-to-air missile batteries and the presence of their radar emissions. The status of fuel tanks and associated plumbing and engine performance might be displayed. The weapons panel of the stores management system might show which offensive stores are available and have been selected. A profusion of status lamps, communications management panel lights, IFF selection panel lights along with annunciators and voice communications from controllers and other ground-based radios assail the pilot's senses. Altogether there is plenty of information. But if it is presented in a confused manner the pilot is not aware of the total situation; both inside the cockpit and outside the aircraft.

Therefore SA is a key factor when considering cockpit systems and equipment in relation to the critical forcing mission conditions. Essentially, SA is enhanced by the provision of a limited set of data on top quality displays. This is where the 'need to know' rule has to be rigorously applied. It is also the basis on which to allocate systems for fully automatic operation.

In the previous chapter mention was made of the HOTAS concept used for the design of the cockpits of the 1980s. This will still apply to the cockpits of the next century. HOTAS helps to keep the pilots to good SA in a fighter/attack aircraft at the highest level. A Direct Voice Input (DVI) system also adds to SA by simplifying the control of systems; such as communications

T-45A Goshawk equipped with the digital Cockpit-21. The interface is based on the HOTAS concept with two multi-function colour CRT displays and a HUD. To the left of the CRT displays is a group of four conventional, pointer-on-dial, flight instruments for use should the electronic displays fail. (McDonnell Douglas)

channel selection. DVI is the subject of research aimed at making it a primary part of the cockpit interface.

Enhancing the visual interface

A number of new concepts have been evaluated and some already incorporated in current fighter/attack aircraft and those programmed to enter service in the next century. These include new and effective techniques for enhancing the

visual interface within and without the aircraft; particularly when the target is beyond visual range or is obscured by environmental conditions.. Examples are FLIR (Forward Looking Infra-Red) and LLTV (Low Light TV). Combined with a laser target designating system, such as TIALD (Thermal Imaging Airborne Laser Designator), FLIR provides an artificial real world display either on the HUD or on the HMD combined with NVG. The RAF used an early version of TIALD with great success when attacking Iraqi targets in the Gulf War. This had been developed in the early 1990s as part of the Nightbird programme at DERA (Defence Evaluation & Research Agency) Farnborough.

At present there are many ideas being evaluated for presenting information to the pilot's eyes:

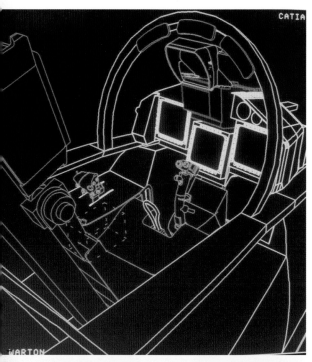

Left: *Computer Aided Design (CAD) enables the cockpit development team to visualise the relative positions of equipment.*
(British Aerospace)

Below: *The DASH helmet-mounted targeting and display system worn by the pilot of an F/A-18. Tactical, attack and flight information is projected onto the visor of the helmet and focused at infinity.*
(McDonnell Douglas)

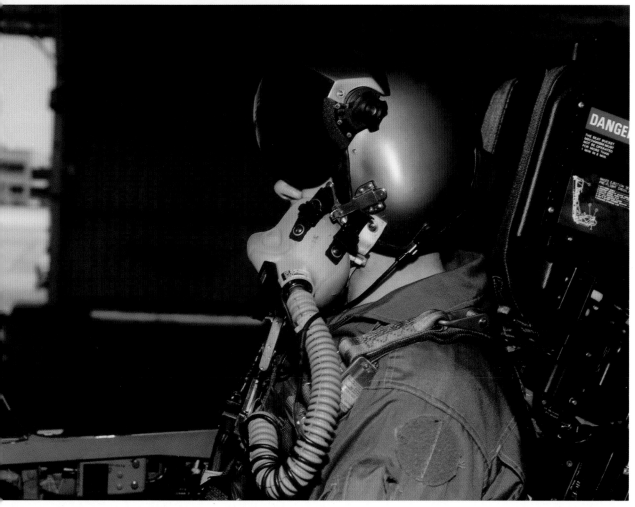

Above: *The pilot of this F-18 is wearing Night Vision Goggles (NVG). These have to be compatible with scanning the instrument panels and when looking through the HUD.*
(McDonnell Douglas)

Right: *The lightweight (150 gm) monocular helmet-mounted ALPHA sight.*
(GEC-Marconi)

Below: *Even the occupant of the back seat in an F-18 is given a comprehensive array of electronic displays.*
(McDonnell Douglas)

An F-18A cockpit with three multi-purpose colour displays. At night or in poor visibility conditions the 'picture' generated by the Forward Looking Infra-Red (FLIR) *can be presented either on one of the 'head down' displays or on the HUD or on both.* (McDonnell Douglas)

Right: Experimental Aircraft Programme (EAP). 'Wall-to-wall' colour electronic displays with peripheral 'soft' keys for selecting the type of information to be presented. Large field-of-view HUD. Many of the details in the cockpit of EAP have been carried over to the cockpit of the Eurofighter.
(British Aerospace)

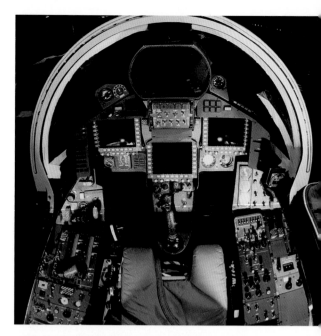

Above: F-22 simulator cockpit for training pilots in the use of the four CRT colour displays and the integrated control panel. Also visible are (left) the throttle levers and (right) the side-mounted control column. The defence display on the left provides a plan view of air and ground threats. In the middle is the primary situation display showing tactical information, tracks, ground positions and the aircraft's sensor search volume. The shape and colour of target icons depict threat identity, track quality and priority. On the right is the secondary attack display giving a plan view of air threats with their altitudes, missile launch-envelopes, weapon steering cues and missile-fly-out paths. The lower display covers stores management, engine and systems information and functions.

The integrated control panel at the top is the interface for the HUD. Two other electronic displays not included in the simulator are (left) for communication and navigation functions and (right) for standby flight instrumentation display.
(Boeing Defense and Space Group)

EF2000 Typhoon. HUD combining glass with minimal support so as to give maximum view ahead; over 90% of information is presented on the three electronic displays and the HUD and many interface functions are executed by Direct Voice Input.
(British Aerospace)

HMDs and retinal imaging systems (RISs) for example. Irrespective of the technology used there are the overriding requirements of freedom of head movement and low weight. The conventional 'bone' dome is already an additional load on the pilot's neck muscles, particularly when subjected to high G effects. Whatever form a helmet of the future takes it must help to maintain the wearer's consciousness, clarity of speech, acuity of hearing and vision during the violent manoeuvres of an agile, 'point in any direction', fighter.

Irrespective of advances which may be made in display technologies during the first decade of the 21st century, the HMD is likely to provide the primary visual interface in the majority of fighter/attack cockpits. An HMD can present FLIR images and flight data and symbology similar to that of a HUD. The HMD can also be used with target designator and aiming systems such as TIALD. An important part of target designator systems research concerns crew workload. These systems have to avoid overloading the crew during critical phases of flight, such as when attacking a heavily defended ground target. It is also just as important to prevent a 'fixation' on the target display to the extent that

the pilot is unaware that the aircraft is no longer keeping to the required trajectory or is too close to the ground. Once again, additional information has to be displayed, such as ground proximity warning. Because a target designator system may not be pointing directly along the aircraft's flight path an additional display on the HUD or HMD is needed to show the pilot the relative bearing of the target.

Mention of ground proximity warning introduces TERPROM. This was developed by British Aerospace in the 1980s. It stands for Terrain Profile Matching. Its principal function is to reduce crew workload and improve navigation and target-finding accuracy. It operates automatically from take-off to touch down and is able to point an aircraft at a selected ground location, including discriminating between a particular span of a bridge. A complex sortie can be planned in advance and 'played back' on a TV so that the crew can check the details and 'rehearse' the

The aft cockpit of the Tornado Integrated Avionics Research Aircraft (TIARA) modified to include a five-inch multi-purpose display and TV display.
(Falcon Aviation/PJC)

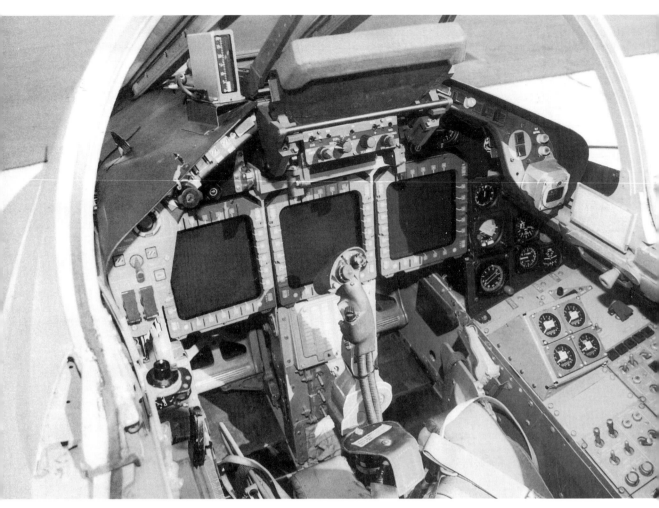

different stages of the flight.

A specific example which presages the cockpit equipment of the 21st century is the UK DERA's AIAH that was evaluated in a Tornado. Acronyms tend to proliferate and annoy but AIAH avoids the long-winded appellation 'Advanced Integrated Avionic Helmet'. This combines life-support, protection, communication and display functions; including FLIR. In the past the pilot's 'bone-dome' was designed just as a protection and communications carapace to the head. Subsequently provision has had to be made for NVGs and HMDs. This bit-by-bit progress has resulted in pilots having to wear bulky and heavy helmets. AIAH provides a lighter and less bulky solution.

The GEC-Marconi Avionics VIPER HMD developed in 1994 was a precursor for interface

Forward cockpit of the Tornado Integrated Avionics Research Aircraft (TIARA) used to evaluate a head-steered forward-looking infra-red and an infra-red search and track systems. An example of using an existing cockpit to study the proposed interface for future aircraft.
(Falcon Aviation/PJC)

equipment of the 21st century. VIPER provides a lightweight binocular visor projected display. The visor on the helmet combines and reflects video, symbology and alphanumerics into the pilot's line of sight as well as real world view enhanced by NVG. The optical design allows the use of a standard spherical curved visor. This has neutral density, partly reflecting combiner coating. The coating ensures high display brightness which at the same time does not distort or attenuate the view of the real world. As the visor is spherical to the pilot's centre of vision, display accuracy is not affected by visor movement. For example the visor can be partly raised without distorting the display. One characteristic of the VIPER HMD is its adaptability to accommodate different eye spacing (the interpupilliary distance). A more recent development in HMD technology is the GEC-Marconi Alpha Sight. This provides the pilot with simple directional arrows which can be used for steering a TIALD and for off-boresight aiming of missiles such as ASRAAM[2] (Advanced Short-Range Air-to-Air Missile). An important feature of the Alpha Sight is it's lightweight and therefore is a step in the right direction away from the tendency to overload the pilot's neck muscles

The modern fighter/attack cockpit can be defined in respect of four principal elements: the human pilot, the AI pilot associate, HOTAS and HUD/HMD. Some of the functions of HOTAS are being passed to DVI and by the next century HMD may give way to RIS. Interactive touch - screen displays are being developed which can be used in high vibration and G conditions for interface functions not allocated to DVI.

In summary, the future man/machine interface in combat aircraft is likely to be an integration of touch screen, DVI, HOTAS and HMD. Depending on the current environmental conditions in the cockpit, each technique has its part to play.

The new aircraft

When aircraft designers start to think seriously about a new military aircraft the first thing they turn to is the list of requirements issued by the customer i.e. the air force. The specification's most important section is that which spells out the operational role of the aircraft. This affects everything related to the cockpit. However, the cost of a military aircraft, measured in millions of dollars, is so great that it often has to perform more than one operational task. The multi-role combat aircraft, as exemplified by the Panavia Tornado and the Eurofighter, were the result of a number of operational and economic factors imposed by the 'owner' nations. With more than one air force having a say in what happened a further complication was faced by the designers. The Tornado's design team, for example, had to

incorporate many new or additional operational modes as the design progressed. The design of the cockpit was very much influenced by the overall 'multi-role' part of the specification. As mentioned, the designers of the F-111 similarly had to serve the sometimes conflicting demand of more than one 'customer' air force.

Different operational roles

The cockpits of military aircraft have to be equipped with controls and information systems to enable the aircraft to be flown by a human pilot during at least two and perhaps most of the following tasks:

air superiority
air defence interception
close support interdiction
interdiction and strike
close air support
tactical reconnaissance
anti-ship strike
long-range ferrying.

These operational tasks will be specified as major features of the requirements promulgated by the air staff of an air force. The UK Air Staff Requirements (ASRs) include, as major design targets for RAF aircraft, the following:

Payload
Operational radius
Ferry range
Performance envelope
Type of weapons.

But this list does not include the cockpit. To do so might unnecessarily inhibit the initial design studies.

A typical requirement, which acknowledges the very hostile air-to-ground war environment, is a 90% probability of a successful strike against a target in one pass irrespective of weather and visibility. This and other requirements directly affect the cockpit design process.

Each of the major design targets will generate specific sets of requirements related to aerodynamics, engines, weapon systems and the avionics. When the design team comes face to face with these major design targets it has to avoid a 'Jack of all trades master of none' aircraft; particularly with a 'multi-role' type.

The cockpits of modern fighter/attack aircraft,

including the multi-role types, have to give the pilot every opportunity to make the best use of the aircraft as a weapon system. Although 'weapon system' is an overworked expression all the same it serves to remind us of the concept that an aircraft's structure, engines, electronics, armament-systems and, of course, the crew and the cockpit, have to work together.

Each has to 'talk', in the electronic sense, with each of the others. As we have seen, in the less complex days of the early decades of aviation, the cockpit and its equipment often took second or even third place to the demands of the aero-dynamics and structural people.

Trade-offs

At some point in the chronology of a new aircraft's evolution the different design teams increasingly start to talk and write about 'trade-offs' and compromises. For example: 'If you decide to lose an inch between frames number 150 and 155 then you'll have to let me run the cross flow pipe behind frame 155 "and so on."'

It is not practicable to devise a table of design priorities and targets, figuratively carved in stone, for cockpit equipment because as the design progresses there may have to be steps backward in order to adjust previously agreed details.

The pilot's view through the cockpit canopy and windscreen of the Eurofighter 2000 is limited only by one structural frame. (British Aerospace)

Those responsible for getting started on the cockpit usually know approximately how much volume they will be allowed in which to accommodate the human pilot, the controls, the instruments and the ejection seat. Nevertheless they know that at all times during the evolution of the new aircraft they will have to fight all the way for every inch and cubic inch. The aero-dynamicists and stealth specialists, along with the engine team, demand optimum shapes and volumes throughout the length of the fuselage including the cockpit area. In the past, when the cockpit and its equipment were often secondary considerations within the total aircraft design process, optimisation of decisions between the structures and systems teams and those responsible for the cockpit was also of secondary importance. Of course, it is easy to criticise with hindsight. Therefore it must be acknowledged that the scarcity of human factors data in earlier years sometimes contributed to inadequate, and some-times dangerous, cockpit interfaces.

The cost

The costs of a cockpit, which includes all the interface equipment, can be a significant propor-tion of total aircraft cost. Approximately the cockpit costs increase with the increase in aircraft versatility. The greater the number of avionic and weapon systems the greater the cost of the instru-mentation and controls. The greater the per-formance of the aircraft the greater the need for

more expensive crew protection. Modern aircrew are themselves a very expensive item of total cost. Their training takes a large slice of an air force's budget. As mentioned, the pilot must be given every opportunity to make the most effective use of the aircraft as a weapon system. At $50 million or more a throw compared with a $10,000 Spitfire, it must not be a case of 'For want of a nail' and so on.

One of the first design stages for a fighter/attack, ejection seat, high-G, cockpit are computer-generated images and arrangements of equipment against which the anthropometric factors can be tested. As with most areas and volumes in an aircraft, there has to be a datum. For the cockpit of an agile fighter this datum is the pilot's eye reference point or datum eye position. This datum is used when determining the required arcs of view by the pilot to see downwards over the nose, to the sides and to the rear. It is also used as the datum for viewing all instruments and controls as well as for the optics of the HUD. An early example was the pin-hole camera used when settling the major dimensions of the cockpit of the AFB1 fighter of 1917.

Design team

The cockpit 'design team' has to work closely with the other specialist groups of designers. The overall goal of the cockpit design team is to produce a control interface that: will provide adequate interchange of information and commands during each of the operational roles for which the aircraft has been designed; will ensure that the human pilot's abilities are used most effectively; will protect and ensure the pilot's safety and recovery in the event of disaster. Not many words but they represent everything that the pilot will need.

Working together

The relationship of the 'four-nation' (Britain, Germany, Italy and Spain) EF2000 (Eurofighter) cockpit design group with other disciplines, systems and requirements provides a useful example of the overall task and of working together.

The cockpit design group interfaced with over

fifteen individual design offices and indirectly with over another twelve concerned with the cockpit. Among the different groups was the Avionics Joint Team. This was responsible for the important displays and controls as well as the weapon systems, the integrated defensive systems and ground support systems. The interface with the Eurofighter main design office was obviously a key operation. Under the heading of power and mechanical systems needed for the cockpit were power generation, crew escape, cockpit environment and life-support systems. Other interested parties included airworthiness and the utilities control system teams. As the cockpit design progressed flight operations and flight test teams became increasingly involved. An important source of 'hands-on' experience was the pool of four fighter pilots from each of the four Eurofighter nations.

The description of the Eurofighter team can be used to emphasise, in general terms, the extent to which the cockpit design of any modern fighter/attack aircraft is very much a co-operative effort by many different specialists design teams. The time when the cockpit often took second or even third place in design resources has long gone. Also the time has gone when specialists in different departments of a design centre worked away in isolation from others: so that late, often very late, in the total aircraft design process they emerged to demand space and services in the cockpit for their particular system. In the past there have been examples of cockpit design by committee when the number of people having an interest in the cockpit became unwieldy. The TSR2 was an aircraft before its time. Its technology was very advanced but the attitude of some ministerial people worked against progress as reported by test pilot Roland Beamont. He recalls a TSR2 'cockpit' committee meeting attended by sixty-one interested persons. One of these gatherings spent hours debating and arguing over the size, wording and position of a switch. As Beamont recalls, when he came to check the cockpit for the first time, the wording on one of the switch labels bore no relationship to its function. All this was in the early 1960s. Since then a more scientific approach has been made to the subject.

One of the methods used to produce the optimum cockpit by a cockpit design team is based on the concept of the 'forcing' set of requirements. Forcing because it forces all detail design decisions towards this primary objective of the design team. Although a number of operational roles may be specified, one of these, along with one particular phase of flight, can be specified as the forcing set of conditions. For example it could be that for an air superiority fighter the combat phase gives the forcing set of conditions.

The less dramatic operational scenario of a reconnaissance flight, during which the aircraft has to be refuelled from aerial tankers, may be the forcing set because of the many hours in which the pilot is confined to one position. At intervals the pilot may have to exercise considerable skill in finding a tanker and keeping station during the fuel transfer. Halfway through the long flight the primary objective of tactical reconnaissance has to be completed. Both these sets of requirements are forcing on the design. And this is where the design team has to keep more than one design target in view. However a stage is reached in the design process when one of the forcing sets becomes the more important.

Each of the different operational roles of an aircraft are subjected to analysis. Each in turn specifies the systems needed to complete a particular type of sortie; each of which will interface directly or indirectly with the cockpit. This process enables the design team to establish the list of interface equipment: such as controls and instruments; in other words all the tactile, visual and aural devices needed to enable the human pilot to be an integrated part of the aircraft as total weapon system. Human factors specialists can provide assessments of aircrew workload over a wide range of operating situations. This data can be incorporated into the forcing set assessment.

The forcing set or forcing operational role/phase can now be determined largely from computer and simulation studies. These can be backed up by the in-flight experience of those who have been concerned with aircraft types that have preceded the new design. The 'forcing' exercise continues in parallel with other design streams such as those of the aerodynamicists, the structures people and the engine company. Eventually they come together and are joined by others. For example, as the aerodynamicists and structural teams begin to firm up their ideas the systems engineers start to 'come on stream' and flow into the general design body. The cockpit, as a specific set of design requirements, begins to take shape. Modern electronic displays provide 'selectable' information. For example, during the search and combat phases en route navigation and engine performance information can be relegated to a secondary area of the displays. Whereas, during start-up, roll-out and take-off engine performance parameters should be presented close to the pilot's forward line of sight. The tactile controls, such as levers, switches and buttons, are classified in groups so that those most frequently used and of great importance are located close to the pilot's hands. Today these criteria are accepted as fundamental design standards. But, in the past they were often neglected.

A member of a fighter/attack aircraft design team emphasised to the author that in a critical path analysis of all the separate design tasks the cockpit was the critical item. Aerodynamics, structures, electrics and utilities systems took significantly less time to design and prove than the cockpit and the machine/human interface systems. After the forcing set or sets of requirements were agreed with the customer air forces the preliminary studies of the interface, even when applying the best available computer technologies, still took a year to complete. Another year was taken up with the building of a prototype rig of the interface elements. If off-the-shelf commercial equipment had not been available the programme would have taken even longer. From the beginning of the design process the demands on those responsible for 'writing' the software increased with each passing month. Eventually generating and proving the interface software became the major time and cost factor within the overall development programme for the new aircraft. It took over two years before the software and hardware, using test rigs, were able to meet the required safety-critical standards.

Although the foregoing is a simplified description of a very complex operation nevertheless it reminds us of the way in which the avionics and associated software dominate the road that leads to the first test flight of a new aircraft.

When the first specifications were issued in the mid-1980s, those responsible for the cockpit design of the Eurofighter 2000, were faced with the following major requirements: the primary role as a single-seat, low-weight, highly-agile, air-superiority fighter; a cockpit interface matched to a weapon system for both 'beyond visual range' and 'close-in' combat situations; a cockpit envelope restricted by the comparatively small size of the aircraft.

To meet the above criteria the cockpit was designed around three fundamental concepts. These were: a centre control column, rather than a side-stick; three head-down colour electronic displays; a head-up display. The displays automatically present information which is appropriate to the current aircraft operating mode. For example, when the parking brake is released the displays show inertial navigation system status and data. The displays also present a list of all actions which have been performed automatically. The concepts of 'need to know' and of limiting the input of information to the pilot, so as to reduce workload and enhance situation awareness, are key cockpit design elements for the Eurofighter. There are few 'pointer-on-dial' instruments in front of the Eurofighter pilot. In the event of a major failure of the electronic display system there are 'standby' displays which are independent of the main instrument systems. These are to the side of the main display panel and provide the pilot with essential flight information to enable the aircraft to be recovered to its base. These display heading, airspeed, altitude, vertical speed, angle of attack and attitude. To save panel space most of the standby displays are stored out of sight until needed behind a hinged panel which displays IFF and other tactical information.

The Eurofighter 2000 will continue as a first-line aircraft with the four nations well into the 21st century. Therefore the cockpit design team has selected wherever possible the most advanced technologies available. One of these is a 'point and shoot' pilot's helmet. The aircraft's computer system provides flight and target information and weapon-aiming data which is projected electronically on the helmet's visor. During air-to-air combat or when attacking a ground target the pilot moves his or her head to bring an aiming mark, displayed on the visor, over the target. When detected each target is automatically allocated an alphanumeric label which then may be used by the pilot to designate that target for attack using the DVI system. The pilot speaks the appropriate DVI command and microseconds later the target appears in the list of current targets on the Multi-function Head Down Display. The pilot may then rapidly allocate one or more weapons to that target using the fast reaction HOTAS controls. When the target comes within a specified range a visual 'SHOOT' cue flashes up on the HMD and the pilot may then use HOTAS to release the weapon. Great care has been taken to select DVI command words which are unlikely to be misrecognised as other command words. The DVI system may still be used in this way even if the target is beyond visual range (BVR).

Under the heading of the abbreviation DVI there are a number of different speech recognition techniques. These include: speaker-dependent and speaker-independent as well as the recognition of isolated words, connected words and continuous speech. A speaker-dependent system has to be programmed to recognise an individual voice. In other words it has to be trained by listening to a vocabulary repeated many times until it has built into its memory a template for every word. When the pilot speaks, the DVI system scans its memory, in microseconds of course, so as to match what it hears with one of the word templates. A number of word protocols have to be used to avoid ambiguities. For example if the pilot says *'Fuel'* the DVI system selects an appropriate subset in anticipation that the next word will specify which tank contents needs to be displayed.

The DVI system developed by Computing Devices Hastings and Smiths Industries for the Eurofighter 2000 is a precursor of the cockpit interface for the 21st century. About twenty-five different functions are controlled by voice command based on a 200-word vocabulary. These include: calling up specific displays on the electronic screens, and selecting radio channels and frequencies. To interface with the DVI system a pilot's voice is 'enrolled' at a ground-based computer station in advance of each flight. The system is able to recognise a pilot's individual voice pattern at all times and in flight can cope with the physical strains placed on the vocal chords by G forces and other stresses imposed on the pilot during combat.

The DVI and the cockpit aural system together with the visor or retinal imaging displays take the HOTAS concept of the 1960s many stages further on in cockpit evolution. Now the cockpit interface is concentrated during critical phases of flight directly in the pilot's eyes. The tactile interface is also changed significantly because some of the pilot's control actions are conveyed by DVI. Air fighting has come a long way from the 1940s, when scientists and pilots first experimented with the idea of combining a CRT display with the reflector gunsight.

When Eurofighter cockpit studies started an appropriate Computer Aided Design (CAD) implementation was not available. This meant that wooden mock ups and anthropometric dummies and models had to be used to verify all decisions concerning dimensions and relative locations of cockpit elements and equipment. Contributing to the design process and of particular value when one of Eurofighter's customers demanded a change, was the Active Cockpit Simulator. The technology of simulation had advanced considerably in ability, realism and range of functions since the time of the Experimental Aircraft Programme (EAP was an experimental aircraft for proving the Eurofighter concept).

The attention given to the human factors aspects of the cockpit design of the Eurofighter 2000 has been far greater than that applied to previous European fighter/attack aircraft. Reducing pilot workload and ensuring the safety of both man and machine remained throughout the design process as major targets. Safety and survivability and therefore certainty of completing a sortie and recovering to base is enhanced by the twin-engine configuration and the quadruplex control system which conveys the pilot's flight control inputs to the control surfaces. This system also leaves the pilot free to concentrate on using the aircraft as a weapon system without fear of stalling or over stressing it. Also contributing to workload reduction is the provision of an intelligent ground proximity warning system.

An interesting item in the cockpit of the Eurofighter 2000 and in the Sukhoi 27 is the 'when all else has failed' button. When pressed this automatically returns the aircraft to a wings level, nose-up attitude with the engines at an intermediate thrust setting. The object of this system is to help a pilot, who may be new to the aircraft, to recover from the effects of disorientation after the application of a high-G manoeuvre. It could also assist an experienced pilot in similar

Clay mock up of throttle grip for a fighter/attack aircraft. A basic ergonomic design step using the human hand and fingers as a mould.
(British Aerospace)

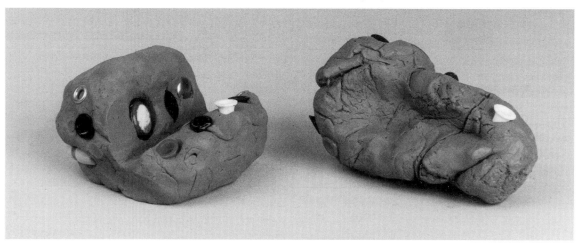

circumstances. An ancestor of this system was used in the Douglas F3D-2 of 1950 (see chapter 5). However, the contemporary of the Eurofighter, the F-22 does not have a 'panic' button to enable a disorientated pilot to command the autopilot to restore the aircraft to straight and level flight.

The layout of the cockpit controls and displays concentrates all the important switches used during air combat or ground attack on the throttle levers and the central control column. As with other recent and proposed combat aircraft, such as the JAS-39, F-22 and JSF, the pilot does not have to 'scan' displays relating to such systems as electrics and fuel, to ensure their correct functioning. These tasks are looked after by the aircraft's mission and vehicle management systems. These will only make their presence felt in the event that something has or is about to go wrong and which needs some action on the part of the pilot, thereby keeping the workload at an acceptable level.

In the Eurofighter the communications subsystem, in conjunction with a dedicated warnings panel, provides a wide range of voice warnings which alert the pilot to the failure of any of the aircraft systems. A dedicated MHDD warnings format then provides procedural instructions on how to deal with a particular failure.

The weapon-aiming in the Eurofighter 2000 centres on a Helmet Mounted Display (HMD) with integrated NVG. The pilot is able to engage targets which are not necessarily directly ahead of the aircraft, in other words 'over the shoulder'. The HMD is used in conjunction with the GEC-Marconi HUD (30 degrees in azimuth and 25 degrees in elevation) and with the three Smiths Industries Head-Down Displays (HDDs). By providing the pilot with three types of visual display situational awareness is maximised. The HDDs can be used to present aircraft navigation, sensor, weapons, engine or systems information. The 'soft' keys mounted around each screen enable the pilot to select a particular set of information on any one of the three displays.

During air-to-air combat the pilot of a Eurofighter and similar types of aircraft are subjected over a short period, perhaps two minutes, to high G effects. When subjected to these effects the pilot must not be deprived of consciousness,

A very early stage in the development of the control column for a fighter/attack aircraft. The designer uses clay, coins and other ready-to-hand items.
(British Aerospace)

of information or of the ability to control the aircraft. Those two minutes may represent the highest level of workload to be experienced across the range of operational tasks for which the aircraft has been designed. Therefore the cockpit and its information systems, such as visual displays and voice systems, must be designed to ensure that the pilot is not deprived of both information and the ability to react to the rapidly changing environment, both inside and outside the cockpit.

Each of the many and individual functions into which cockpit equipment may be divided is important. Each contributes to the primary design objective. However, it is important to remember that during the design process the need

In addition to CAD visualisations and drawings a wooden mock up is built so that real human pilots can check body clearances and accessibility to all controls. This is an early mock up of the cockpit of the Eurofighter 2000.
(British Aerospace)

for some functions may be transient. An advance in technology can make any one of them redundant and to retain it might hinder overall progress toward the optimum cockpit. The cockpit designer has to cultivate an attitude of mind that recognises this.

The cockpit designer and the design team must ensure that all the available technologies, schemes and devices, of which there may be many, are assessed. None must be dismissed just because it appears not to be directly applicable to a particular type of cockpit. There is always something to be learnt from the fringes of technology. Experience will enable the design

team to make use of or discard ideas in the light of progress.

For example, and this is not an unlikely concept, the overall aircraft operating conditions may predicate a no-cockpit design. Of course, this would not mean that the 'cockpit' designers are out of a job. Far from it. They now have to turn their skills to the remote control position which in turn may require the solving of some difficult interface and human factors problems. Of course, they will then no longer be constrained by volume or weight limitations and the need to protect a human operator against an extreme environment.

Pilot experience

In the first decade of aviation the designer was often the test pilot as well. As aircraft became more complex the test or experimental pilot had to take a less prominent role during the early stages of a new design. Under the stress of war, when there was little time in which to analyse the details of a new cockpit, there emerged some dreadful examples of how not to arrange and position controls and instruments. In many new aircraft the 'design office' looked at what had been done before and decided that it would do.

Sixty years ago an operational pilot would rarely be afforded the chance to comment on the design of a new cockpit at the 'drawing board' stage. Sometimes the company's own test pilot had no say in what went where. In more recent decades it has been accepted that those whose primary place of work will be the cockpit need to have a say in its design: not half way through the process but from the beginning. Therefore the aerodynamicists, structural and systems engineers, stressmen, propulsion specialists and the instrument and controls designers have been joined not only by human factors people but most importantly by operational aircrew with recent experience of combat flying. The experience of air force pilots is now an essential contributor to the overall design process of a cockpit. With the Eurofighter the user air forces each provided experienced pilots to a working party charged with assessing and monitoring the progress of all the cockpit design features. Each of the participating companies flight operations department test pilots were also included in the overall cockpit design process.

Information in the interface

Just as with the commercial aircraft flight deck, the military cockpit now includes a number of keyboards and keys on the periphery of the electronic displays. Not only are there many of these keys, there is also the facility afforded the pilot of being able with one keystroke to change completely the functions of all the other keys. However, the pilot may get out of step with the pages of the data base. This problem is highlighted if we consider an old-fashioned cockpit equipped only with 'conventional' electromechanical instruments. Each of these is dedicated to only one or at the most a few functions. Their information set and format is unvarying and, unless there is a failure, is always in front of the pilot. The pilot does not have to 'call

Intelligent flat panel control/display unit for a military transport aircraft. This provides the interface for all sortie, navigation and flight management functions.
(Smiths Industries)

up' hidden information.

By the end of the 1970s it became clear that the days of the pointer-on-dial 'clock type' instruments were numbered. The electronic multipurpose, all colour, display screens took over. Today the majority of first-line combat aircraft as well as most transport aircraft are equipped with 'wall-to-wall' electronic displays in the cockpit.

Until the advent of the electronic display the instrument designer was constrained by the limitations of electro-mechanical technology. In general, this meant that the majority of instruments were pointer-on-dial. These presented information in a way which many ergonomists argued was intuitive. In fact it was derived from the age of steam. A pointer was arranged so that with increasing values, such as pressure, it moved clockwise round the dial. Eventually the aircraft airspeed indicator pointer also moved clockwise for increasing value. Although there was an anomaly in the case of the altimeter where the pointer, knowing it was part of a barometer, moved anti-clockwise for increasing height i.e. reducing pressure. This was not internationally corrected until the 1930s. One area of conflict among many and of great concern to pilots, is how should information be formatted so that it is presented without any ambiguities? An important example comes from the debates on the apparently simple task of depicting changes in airspeed and altitude.

When solid-state electronic instruments were developed in the late 1960s these offered a vertical scale or 'tape' presentation. If the reference mark were fixed then should the tape move upward or downward for increasing values? In other words as an aircraft ascended should the reference mark appear to move up the scale of increasing values because the tape moved downward so as to expose ever higher numeral values from the top? Or, should the tape move upward to expose higher values from the bottom of the display? There were serious disagreements between pilots and instrument designers. The foregoing is just one of a number of problems that had to be solved before the technology of displaying information to a pilot could embrace the needs of the 21st century. Existing techniques may not suffice for the next century when the whole environment of the man-machine interface will change because of hazards, accelerations and limitations to the human physique and mental abilities imposed by the new generation of air vehicles.

Instrument and cockpit lighting

Since the earliest days of night flying there have been many different types of lighting in the cockpit. The subject is very much one of 'horses for courses'. The requirements of a transport flight deck are likely to be very different from those of a fighter/attack cockpit. Some instruments require greater illumination than others and therefore it is not easy to decide on a system of overall illumination. The important requirement that any system of instrument illumination or floodlighting (for map reading) must be compatible with night vision when searching for targets is obvious. However there have been many different solutions to the problem. This is why it is dangerous to make a statement on cockpit lighting which is applicable to all types of aircraft and to all types of aircraft use. For example when NVGs are used the wearer must be able to switch

from the external view to the instrumental view without the need for the NVGs being blinded by the interior lighting. It may be found, for example, that the majority of instruments should be given blue-green lighting and warning indicators orange-red.

Selection by touch

One aspect of modern electronic instrument technology is the use of the touch screen. The normal CRT or AMLCD screen has an additional coating formed able to detect the position of a finger and relate it to a specific item displayed on the screen. This is an alternative to using 'soft' keys on the periphery of a display or DVI. This seems a very good idea, however there are major drawbacks. When considering touch screens for the Gripen, Saab discovered that the sensitive coating becomes worn and insensitive after a time because of the friction and dirt of the gloved finger. And, in high-G manoeuvres a pilot finds it very difficult, if not impossible, to reach and touch. The same experience was reached by the designers of the F-22 cockpit. The HOTAS concept is very much related to high-G conditions. Of course, in high G conditions a pilot may not only be unable to move the limbs but, at 6 G and above, suffer from G-LOC (G induced Loss of Consciousness).

Single or multi-crew?

The forcing set is very critical in the design of an agile fighter/attack aircraft when a decision has been taken to go for a single-pilot cockpit. The one-pilot, multi-role, aircraft cockpit has to be designed with extreme care and attention to every detail and to every conceivable set of circumstances so as to avoid excessive workload during critical phases of flight. A number of significant air superiority, interdiction and air defence fighters now in air force use are two-seat types. However, the ability to share the workload among the two crew members does not, as might be thought, ease the overall cockpit design problem. Worksharing between the two occupants has its own particular set of problems; for example there are many 'who does what?' questions to be answered.

In a two-seat fighter/attack aircraft of the 1960s the pilot's tasks could have included, in addition to flying the aircraft, the monitoring of the engines and the different systems, such as fuel and electrics, defensive and tactical visual scanning of the air space, visually or electronically acquiring a target, selecting an appropriate weapon and completing an attack. The tasks of the occupant of the second seat could have included navigation and communication, scanning the air space, target acquisition, weapon selection, delivery and control. Some of the tasks could only be completed by one of the crew members, others by either. In practice there was a grey area between the two in which 'who does what?' depended on immediate circumstances; such as visibility conditions, availability of information, type of target and enemy reaction. The contribution of the second 'seat' to workload reduction and operational efficiency did not always offset the cost of structural and systems complexity and performance loss. Side-by-side seating was specified for the Grumman A-6 and the F-111 with the electronics officer sitting to the right of the pilot. As in the F-111, this economised in controls and displays because some could be reached and seen by both crew members. However, among the many fighter/attack/close support aircraft of the past five decades the majority have had tandem seating.

There is a 'two-crew' argument that the psychology of 'two is company' can be an important factor in an emergency situation or in the face of intense electronic and physical countermeasures. The side-by-side arrangement may be of even greater psychological benefit. In the past thirty years the advances in communications, electronic displays, automatic 'intelligent' systems, target acquisition and weapon delivery systems have negated many of the reasons for needing a two-person crew in fighter/attack aircraft. The modern cockpit designed and equipped for maximum pilot situational awareness is very different from that of the Phantom and Tornado.

Anthropometrics

Having decided on the general shape of the cockpit and its openable canopy the first and in many ways one of the crucial design steps, is applying anthropometrics, human body shape and dimensions. These factors include reach, and particular consideration to a pilot's ability to operate controls when subjected to high-G. They also have to cater for variations of the buttock to knee dimension among the range of aircrew.

The anthropometric data used to determine the amount of room needed confirms what we all know. Aircrew are not of a standard height, leg and arm reach, torso/leg proportions and other critical dimensions. Yet the cockpit must allow for a reasonable variation of body dimensions among those who will fly a new aircraft as well as fly other types. As with the simple determination of an average among a number of values, when we eliminate the greatest and the smallest before averaging the remainder, so with the aircrew population. The cockpit will not be expected to allow for giants or midgets.

A basic design consideration is an obvious one. This is that all instruments and controls must be

Inboard profile of pilot in the cockpit of the Saab JAS39 Gripen indicating the seat inclination and the view ahead in the vertical plane. This drawing emphasises the need to pull the pilot's legs back automatically against the seat during the ejection sequence. (Author)

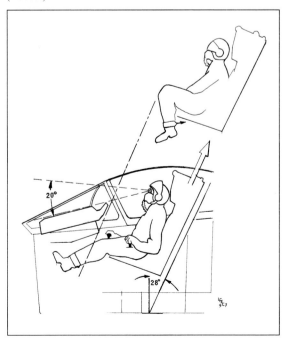

157

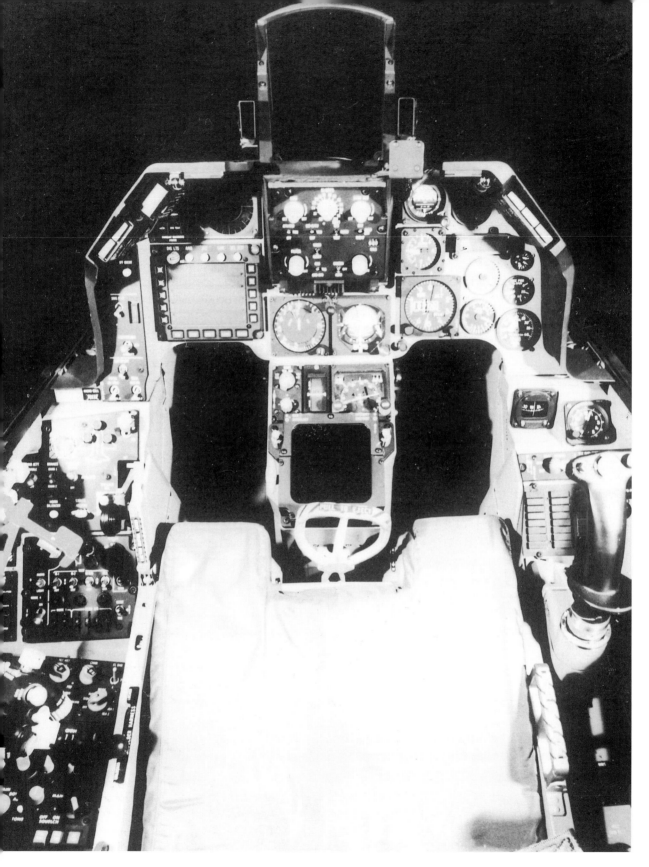

within sight and reach of the pilot when seated in the normal position. The volume which contains all the distances out to which the pilot's limbs and fingers can reach, without excessive stretching, can conveniently be called the ergosphere. Anthropometric considerations and decisions are very much dependent on the fundamental interface choices of central-stick or side-stick?, HUD or HMD? and HOTAS or no HOTAS? They are also dependent on the degree to which the seat is reclined from the vertical.

In the 1980s Saab considered the use of a side-stick for the JAS39 Gripen. Among the reasons given for adopting a conventionally located control column were: the Swedish Air Force wanted its pilots to be able to use the left hand in an emergency and experience of the F-16's side-stick by Swedish pilots had produced unfavourable comments. Furthermore a side-stick control pedestal, along with an arm rest, displaced the normal right-side controls panel; the inhabitants of which could not be found room elsewhere in the cockpit.

These and other design decisions are all part of a number of circles of cause and effect. For example, reclining the seat too much, in order to alleviate G effects on the pilot, takes up valuable fuselage space as well as complicating the relationship between the pilot's eye-reference position and the field of view available through the HUD. It can also affect ejection seat design and the ejection clearance envelope. Saab settled on a pilot's seated position in the Gripen inclined back 22 degrees from the vertical and high set rudder pedals to mitigate the adverse effects of 9G manoeuvres.

Some air forces provide opportunities for females to become fighter/attack pilots. During WWII, with only a very few exceptions, women had only flown in combat in the Soviet air forces and as fighter ferry pilots in the USAAF and RAF. During the design of the cockpit of the Eurofighter the question of female dimensions was raised. The designers were instructed that the cockpit dimensions had to fit the 5th to 95th percentiles range of the pilot population of the four participating countries. It so happened that when that part of the specification was written there were no females in the fighter pilot population. British Aerospace, responsible for the cockpit, pointed out that if there were to be some female Eurofighter pilots then they would either have to fit the existing cockpit or there would have to be a re-design to cater for a small population of pilots having particular needs and dimensions. One of the problem factors arising from provision for a female pilot was the tendency for the eyes of a female to be set closer together than those of the average male. This was particularly relevant to the fields of view when using aiming systems. To put the 'female' pilot subject into perspective it is interesting to note that in the RAF in the early 1990s, out of a total of about 2,700 pilots, only around a dozen were female and of those few only two flew high-performance aircraft.

Physiological stresses

In both civil and military aircraft the human pilot has to be protected from the physiological stresses imposed by the aircraft. Such stresses are present in civil aircraft but usually at a much lower level of effect. Whereas in the highly manoeuvrable combat aircraft, whose airframe is designed to withstand G loads as high as 10 or even higher, the loads, particularly on the pilot's neck and extremities, can be sufficiently severe to prevent movement.

Other stresses are those imposed by fatigue, vibration, noise, atmospheric partial pressure and extremes of temperature. Each of these has a resulting effect related to the length of exposure. Fatigue is more often associated with extended range operations (EROs) in transport aircraft and not with combat aircraft. Contributing to fatigue is the level of activity: even though for a time a high level of activity disguises the onset of mental fatigue and to some extent muscle stress. Therefore it is not practicable to set levels of fatigue other than in crude terms such as the

Opposite: Cockpit of an F-16. The semi-reclining seat limits the instrument panel space above the pilot's feet. The HUD and its up-front control panel and the two CRT displays are an example of the move in the late 1970s away from conventional 'clock' type displays. The F-16 was one of the first to have a side-stick control. Both the side-stick and the rudder pedals are of the force-sensing type requiring minimal movement of hand and feet. The reason why there is no windscreen frame visible is because the canopy is a one-piece, frameless, unit.

length of a flight or the number of sorties completed in 24 hours. The general case is limited to comparative statements. The peaks which interrupt the steady downturn of the pilot's level of concentration, awareness and accuracy of response to events are nature's ability to effect a temporary recovery. Fatigue as such is not always used as a parameter because it does not necessarily occur independently of other factors. Fatigue can be the overall result of the deterioration of many discrete factors. An example of consideration for reducing aircrew stress and fatigue is the cockpit of the Sukhoi 34. The K-36DM ejection seats are reported to have a built-in massage facility. Furthermore, a toilet and galley are located abaft the seats and there is

GQ Aeroconical Type 5000 parachute for use with Martin-Baker ejection seats. This inflates in one second.
(GQ Defence Equipment Ltd)

space between the seats for one crew member to lie down and rest during a long sortie.

Ejecting

There is a set of specialised requirements to cover ejection. The volume swept by the seat and the pilot's body during ejection may prevent the design team from installing cockpit equipment in certain areas. In the F-4 navigator's cockpit there are examples of equipment (radar display unit) which retracts as part of the ejection seat sequence. The ejection seat design may also have to allow for a reclining position in order to mitigate the adverse effects of G. However a variable inclination seat takes up more space. In general the cockpit dimensions most affected by the ejection seat and a reclining position for the pilot are those in the fore and aft direction: although it is also important to allow room at the sides to prevent the pilot's protective clothing from being damaged during ejection. In addition to the restrictions imposed on controls and instruments by the ejection clearances a significantly reclined seat limits the size of control and display panels.

As we have seen, trade-offs and compromises enter the cockpit design scene early on. The ergospheres for both normal and 'ejection' conditions impinge on the desired areas and positions of displays as well as on the location of controls. All these have to be 'traded off' against the optimum arcs of vision: and often against each other. Because the perfect is rarely obtainable the design team has to accept a number of compromises.

Getting in

Naturally great attention is paid during the cockpit design process to aircrew safety of which the ejection seat is a key element. But what about getting up and into the cockpit? Modern aircrew can be encumbered by a survival suit, anti-G garments, a large and bulky helmet, and Nuclear, Biological and Chemical (NBC) protective gear, plus other items of equipment festooned on the body. The sill of the Eurofighter's cockpit, for example, is ten feet above the ground. Means have to be considered for helping aircrew to 'mount-up'. Panavia Tornado crews complained that there were no built-in access steps on the side of the fuselage.

Whatever means is adopted it must provide a quick and easy way of gaining the cockpit. This is very important for aircrew 'at readiness' as part of a quick-reaction squadron. To avoid having to sit for an hour or two in the cockpit they should be in a blast-proof and NBC secure ready-room close to the aircraft in comparative comfort. The final action at the end of the sprint from the ready-room must be simple and quick. Thunderbirds may have had the right idea.

Computer Aided Design

From about 1990 onward there has been an alternative to the laborious and sometimes acrimonious trade-off games. Computer Aided Design (CAD) has come to the aid of the design team. Using CAD techniques every dimension and the full range of anthropometric limits can be adjusted and readjusted, time and time again, until the optimum cockpit is achieved. The proposed cockpit can be viewed on a computer screen from every angle. Each item of equipment can be moved around until it is in its optimum location relevant to every other item and to the crew.

However, despite the versatility of CAD, including the ability to animate human movements when operating or selecting controls the results and knowledge are only as good as the data provided by its programmers. A 'CAD' cockpit may still include mistakes and impracticable ideas. Therefore it is still desirable to build a mock-up so that a human can interface with the new cockpit. Every conceivable limb and head movement must be gone through to check the suitability of control types and positions and the visibility of the displays across the full range of lighting conditions, interior reflections, and to check that the required arcs of view have been achieved. These checks must also include the processes of getting into and out of the cockpit.

Cockpit position

With jet propelled aircraft the position of the cockpit or flight deck need not necessarily have any relationship to the position of the engines.

However with a propeller-driven aircraft there are a number of requirements intended to prevent damage and injury to the cockpit, its systems and to the flight crew should a propeller blade become detached.

A typical set of design safety requirements may specify that in a multi-engine transport aircraft no part of the control interface should be located in the region between the plane of rotation of a propeller and the surface generated by a line passing through the hub and subtending an angle of five degrees fore and aft of the plane of rotation of the propeller.

A fundamental requirement is the provision of adequate arcs of vision for the crew matched to the role of the aircraft. The single-seat pilot must be able to see upward and to the sides over large angles. It is just as important that the pilot can see downward and forward to each side of the aircraft's nose. In most fighter attack aircraft these arcs of view are adequate. However, in canard-equipped aircraft there can be a design conflict between the position of the foreplanes and the pilot's insistence that there are adequate arcs of view forward and downward. Both the Saab Gripen and the Israeli Lavi have the canard wings positioned so as not to obstruct unduly the pilot's arcs of view.

Structural design

In the first three decades of flight there was no need to provide windscreen frames strong enough to withstand the air loads of flight greater than about Mach 0.5. With the unpressurised fuselages unusual windshield shapes could be used. From the earliest years of the enclosed cockpit designers have endeavoured to eliminate as far as possible reflected light from instrument illumination. For example some designers specified reverse-raked forward windscreens.

Until the 1940s cockpit canopies and flight deck fenestration were provided primarily to protect the crew from the air flowing over the aircraft and from rain, hail and snow. Windscreen structures and canopies did not have to be designed to resist other than moderate loads. Over the years increasing emphasis has been placed upon resistance to bird strikes. A typical set of modern design standards specify that the

161

windscreen of transport aircraft and the supporting structures immediately in front of the pilots must resist collapse or penetration by a large bird when the aircraft is flying at cruising speed at sea level. In addition to resisting bird strikes the forward part of the cockpit canopy of a fighter/attack aircraft must continue to provide the pilot with adequate forward visibility after being struck by hailstones.

Aerodynamic and electronic sensor viewing 'windows' requirements usually dictate optimum nose profiles and cross-sections. Set against these are the minimum arcs of view required by the pilot. Therefore to some extent design interaction among the details of the extreme nose, the cockpit area and the fairing of the cockpit lines into the maximum diameter of the fuselage has to be a compromise. Essentially a flight deck window or cockpit canopy is just another discontinuity in the otherwise unbroken contiguous array of structural frames and longitudinal members and their stabilising areas of skin. It goes without saying, that strength must be achieved without excessive weight and, most importantly, without the use of thick window or canopy frames.

The cockpit represents a discontinuity in the otherwise aerodynamically smooth shape of the fuselage. The large opening in the structure is often of irregular shape. It presents, therefore, special design problems; particularly when it comes to diverting loads around windows.

Structural design for pressurisation

Apart from the structural loads which have to be resisted by the frames, the transparencies themselves have to resist pressurisation loads and other effects such as aerodynamic heating. The materials which form the 'sandwich' of a transparency, particularly plastics, are sensitive to temperature, the rate at which loads vary, the duration of the loads, exposure to the elements and ageing. The materials must both achieve and retain, despite the need for double curvatures and acute refractive angles, the desired optical qualities. The materials must also resist loads and environmental effects so as to avoid distortion of the sight line when the pilot is landing the aircraft or using an aiming system. The material must also be consistently compatible with the use of NVGs.

Modern computer-based stress analysis techniques result in structures having minimum weight for maximum strength and life. In general, structural design for an aircraft now provides multiple path redundancy to enhance integrity. However although stress analysis can be applied to the frames of a window they cannot be applied with the same degree of accuracy to plastic transparencies whose structural characteristics are far less amenable to analysis. Compared with plastics, glass has greater resistance to environmental effects. However its structural characteristics may vary considerably from one batch to another. And also, compared with plastics, glass is heavy and there are limitations to the amount of curvature acceptable. Adding to the difficulties of fenestration design are the unknown and uncontrollable factors of production of both glass and plastic windows. Consideration must be given to the in-service fatigue and chemical deterioration characteristics. Their structural integrity depends very much on the production techniques used by the manufacturer when forming, trimming, machining and cementing on edge reinforcement. These are in addition to the control of the heat treatment processes. Altogether the elusive characteristics and performance of glass and plastics has forced designers to adopt empirical solutions to fenestration problems; particularly with the design of the forward windows in a cockpit. Therefore there is no all-embracing set of design formula from which to derive shapes, dimensions and parameters.

The 'sandwich'

Windscreens for flight decks and for the forward surface of a military cockpit canopy are usually a composite design of glass and plastic. The exterior surface of glass resists abrasion and has good thermal conductivity while the inner plastic element provides the resistance to impact from bird strikes. A typical transport aircraft windscreen consists of a glass surface ply and a stretched plastic load-carrying ply made up of two separate vinyl layers. Each of the inner vinyl elements is able to retain the integrity of the window under pressurisation loads in the event of the failure of the glass and the other vinyl layer.

Laminated safety glass, i.e. a sandwich of glass

and plastic, at one time required an accurately machined frame in order to avoid local stressing of the glass. However later developments introduced the concept of extending the plastic inner layer beyond the edge of the glass. This allows the window to be secured in position by clamping it directly to the frame. The plastic edge permits tight clamping without over stressing the glass. At the same time this technique avoids any aerodynamic or manoeuvring loads being applied to the glass should the frame be distorted. This method also has the advantage that it is no longer necessary to machine the frame to extremely tight tolerances.

There are two principal techniques for producing the glass used for a 'sandwich'. These are semi-tempered and fully-tempered. Semi-tempered glass is plate glass which has been polished and then subjected to heat treatment in order to increase its strength up to four times that of commercial glass. Fully-tempered glass is obtained when polished plate glass is given even greater heat treatment in order to increase its strength to over ten times that of commercial glass. Fully-tempered glass has to have all

bending, cutting and edge grinding operations completed before tempering. The final laminated transparency is achieved by the addition of vinyl and plastic layers along with a conductivity layer for heating.

An alternative to the glass and vinyl sandwich is polycarbonate. This material has the particular advantage that it can resist high temperatures. Compared with vinyl, a polycarbonate transparency softens as the temperature increases while retaining its strength at low temperatures. This characteristic together with ductility provides exceptional impact strength as well as allowing polycarbonate sheets to be formed into complex shapes with compound curvatures. Polycarbonate is therefore especially useful. The F-16's one-piece canopy without any forward framework is a good example of the canopy designer's and manufacturer's skills.

This illustrates two particular aspects of modern fighter cockpit design: the large size of the canopy with minimum supporting structure; and the considerable volume taken up by the ejection seat.
(Smiths Industries)

The strength of polycarbonate canopies is such that they only need a minimum of supporting structure. Military pilots are given good visibility over a wide angle, uninterrupted by supporting structure other than the frame of the windscreen. A thin extra hard coating is applied to both the inside and outside surfaces of polycarbonate canopies to protect them from cleaning solvents and abrasive dust. There are a number of different combinations or sandwich layers for cockpit canopies in use among military aircraft types. Some have as many as six different layers. A typical combination is: an outer 'hard' layer, an acrylic followed by an interlayer and then the principal layer formed from poly-carbonate. Another protective 'hard' layer forms the innermost surface. A fine metallic film, such as gold, can be used to reflect electronic emissions.

A modern fighter/attack aircraft cockpit canopy has an area of about 5m squared (50 sq.ft). This self-supporting area is subject to extremes of temperature along with aerodynamic and pressurisation load variations. At extremely high temperatures, such as when an aircraft is parked on a 30°C day in direct sunlight, the canopy will expand upwards and severely stress the bottom edges at the sides. At the other extremes of temperature the canopy will shrink and stress its forward and aft fastenings. The canopy is subjected to aerodynamic heating in high speed flight, and to anti-ice heat and the effects of other vision retention devices which increase the temperature gradient across the glass/vinyl/ sandwich. A large canopy which hinges upwards is subjected to an air load if the aircraft is taxied fast with the canopy open.

Vision retention

The four principal methods of keeping the windscreen clear are: mechanical (rubber-on-

The skill of the large one-piece canopy makers is exemplified by the two-seat F-16 cockpit.
(GEC Avionics)

glass, power-driven wipers); gold film heating elements as part of the 'sandwich'; aerodynamic techniques; and hot air blast (sometimes combined with chemical spray).

Sealing, locking and jettisoning

In earlier times the cockpit canopy was a comparatively simple arrangement of frames, transparencies and sliding or hinged elements so that it could be retracted or hinged to one side. Pressurisation required inflatable sealing systems, heavier transparencies and heating. Significant reductions in the time available in which to escape from the cockpit required canopy jettison systems and later miniature detonation cord (MDC) attached to the canopy and triggered as part of the seat ejection sequence.

The 'stealthy' cockpit

The 1991 Gulf War provided for the first time the opportunity to employ three new technologies simultaneously with devastating effect on the enemy. The USAF used night air attacks to eliminate key Iraqi targets. The weapons used were guided bombs launched from F-117s. The technologies were the imaging infra-red stabilised laser target marking system and 'smart', active target-seeking, bombs used in conjunction with the stealth characteristics of the F-117s. These technologies combined to affect directly the design of the cockpit and the tasks of the pilot.

The stealth shape of the F-117 is made up of straight lines rather than the smooth curves of other aircraft. The straight lines and flat surfaces help to reflect radar energy in such a way that the echo signals are attenuated and dispersed away from the source of the impinging energy. The surface of the F-117 is also covered in radar absorbent material and the cockpit transparencies have a gold film to limit electronic emissions penetrating into the cockpit. The nose and cockpit canopy are formed into a point by straight lines in both elevation and plan. The pilot's preferred all-round view has had to give way to the demands of stealth. This stealth shape limits the pilot's arcs of view particularly when banking the aircraft in a turn. The view astern is also restricted. Therefore the pilot of an F-117

has to concentrate on getting to the target and cannot be too much concerned over what is happening to each side. In fact when flying in formation at night the aircraft have to be flown line astern because of the limited view on each beam.

When a laser-guided bomb is released the pilot has to hold the target in the display of the infra red attack and delivery system until the bomb strikes the target. The electronic displays and the automatic flight and engine control systems enable the pilot to acquire the target visually or electronically, release the bomb and guide it to the target. Without the automatic systems the pilot will not have time in which to carry out the weapon guidance tasks.

Referring back to an earlier era in military flying, the disorientation experienced, sometimes with fatal results, by WWII pilots at night also affects F-117 pilots. As one pilot comments: 'Accidents at night are often attributed to a pilot becoming spatially disoriented, a factor of working head-down with the infra-red attack and delivery system while trying to fly the aircraft. The cockpit's limited visibility exacerbates this tendency. Routine use of the autopilot and autothrottles mitigates this problem'.[3]

'Fighting transport' cockpits

The fighter/attack cockpit tends to attract greater interest than those in other types of aircraft. What of the cockpits of multi-engine tactical and strategic transports? Many tended to be little different from their civil counterparts. However, the increasing demand for aircraft which can operate close to the ground war has resulted in a number of specialised transports. These require cockpits equipped for their specialised role. An important aircraft in this category is the Lockheed C-130.

The cockpit of the first C-130 reflected its early 1950s vintage. Successive versions of this ubiquitous multi-purpose, four-engine, load carrier have had improvements to the type and quality of the instruments. navigation equipment and systems management. The aircraft required a flight deck crew of four. The latest version, the C-130J, has a completely redesigned cockpit with displays and controls arranged to be in sight and

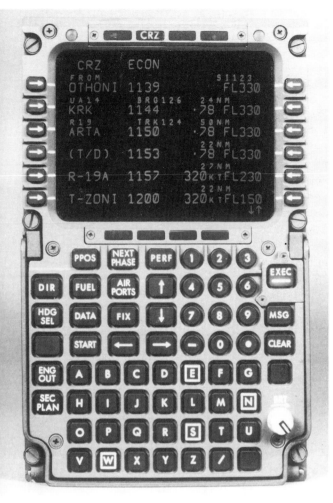

CRZ
CRZ   ECON
FROM   S 1123
OTHONI 1139   FL330
UA14   BRG126   24NM
KRK   1144   ·78 FL330
R19   TRK124   50NM
ARTA   1150   ·78 FL330
                    22NM
(T/D) 1153   ·78 FL330
                    27NM
R-19A 1157   320ᴋᴛFL230
                    22NM
T-ZONI 1200   320ᴋᴛFL150

A typical flight management system display and control panel used in transport aircraft. This unit can be used to command the aircraft's flight systems to execute the desired route and vertical profile to a waypoint.
(Smiths Industries)

reach of the flight crew of just two pilots. Four six-inch by eight-inch multi-function liquid crystal colour displays and head-up displays for both pilots provide the primary visual interface. The HUDs display flight and navigation information leaving the head-down displays for tactical data and aircraft systems. For the greater part of a sortie the pilots use the HUD for both 'visual' flight and 'instrument' flight conditions. Should either of the HUDs fail then flight information is automatically switched to one of the head-down displays.

Although the C-130J is a two-pilot aircraft crew workload has not been increased. Compared with flying the earlier versions, workload has been reduced. Each pilot has four alternative methods of monitoring and controlling all aircraft systems. This is a vital feature of the cockpit of an aircraft which frequently is required to go 'into harm's way' when one or more areas of the control interface could be damaged. Contributing to workload reduction are the replacement of the many systems which required constant monitoring in the earlier C-130s by total system automatic management. This works on the 'need to know' principle so that unless something is about to go wrong or has gone wrong the crew can concentrate on completing the programmed sortie. Along with HUDs the automatic management systems, including thrust control, allow the pilots time to make 'eyeball' searches, particularly when flying low level.

The upgrading of the C-130's systems and cockpit takes the aircraft into the 21st century.

Artificial intelligence

An artificial intelligence (AI), or intelligent knowledge-based system (IKBS), can be an important adjunct to the cockpit systems. In its most advanced concept it is a computer which acts as an assistant pilot. The 'AI' pilot alerts and advises the human pilot about the best of a number of available options following aircraft problems or changes to the tactical situation.

An AI system merges human knowledge and experience with the computer. Such a system emulates human thought and reasoning processes by absorbing the knowledge and experience of many experts, such as aircrew, engineers and tacticians so that the system performs as well as the best of the experts. The knowledge base of the AI can be constantly updated. For example, during each aircraft sortie the AI system stores each of the crew's decisions. The successful or most appropriate are used to reinforce the knowledge base. Any wrong decisions or actions are also noted. An AI system figuratively sits beside the pilot and provides instant answers to complex problems as they arise. It works in parallel with other aircraft systems which have a degree of AI. For example, systems such as an

Electrical Power Management System (EPMS) use a form of AI to react instantly to events, such as a loss of electrical power following damage, by switching electrical loads without the intervention of the human crew.

In the 1980s AI looked very promising but in the following decade there were few examples of AI systems in aircraft cockpits. Although progress was made with systems able to give a pilot advice and answers in non-real time, real-time proved more difficult. In non-real time an AI system can provide answers, such as the correct remedial action, to questions relating to problems with aircraft systems. However, in order to contribute to situation awareness in the high-speed environment of air combat an AI, knowledge-based system, has to work in real-time and give instantaneous advice and answers. AI, at all levels, has to be able to keep a pilot informed fully on a 'need to know' basis. A primary function is that of keeping pilot workload to acceptable limits. This is where an AI system becomes part of a mission management system (MMS). In the UK the avionics companies work with the Defence Evaluation & Research Agency in developing AI-based MMSs. From the cockpit interface point of view and in relation to earlier comments about more avionics tending to increase rather than decrease pilot workload, an important part of an MMS's function is workload reduction. An MMS also needs a large area of electronic display to be an effective provider of information. Which prompts the question: can a single-seat aircraft pilot afford to check the MMS displays when flying at 250 feet and at 800 knots? Most likely not and therefore MMS information may have to be presented aurally.

Humans make mistakes. Pilots and other aircrew have and will continue to make mistakes. Part of an AI system's function is to prevent mistakes on the part of the human crew. AI is computer-based and depends for its integrity and accuracy on its software. The software however is also human-generated and therefore is not infallible. This could mean that even though an AI system has built-in self-checking functions there may be the occasional error. Therefore the system must be designed and its software written so that the probability of an error will be no greater than that of the human crew.

At the end of the 20th century

Today the cockpit interface in tactical aircraft provides the pilot with: an accurate indication of aircraft position in three-dimensional space; a display giving advanced indications of obstructions, such as pylons and wires, when flying 'nap of the earth' sorties; an instantaneous display and warning of hostile radar and infra-red emissions and missiles which have 'locked-on' to the aircraft; along with audio and visual warning and advisory messages to prevent inadvertent collision with other aircraft. In addition there are many automatic systems which can respond in milliseconds to events, such as potential systems failures. Within the overall mission and aircraft management system there is the stores/weapons control sub-system which simplifies the pilot's task when it is necessary to make a split second choice between different types of weapons.

Military transport aircraft cockpits of today have avionic systems which maintain the crew's situation awareness, provide sortie management, including precise navigation and timing for air drops, search and rescue and the many other tasks expected of modern airforce aircraft of all types.

Notes

1. Hirst, M. *MILTECH* 6/83. p. 14.
2. *Aerospace* Jan edn. p. 22.
3. (1996) *Aviation Week & Space Technology*, 29 April edn. p. 45.

CHAPTER SEVEN

YEAR 2000 AND BEYOND

For nearly 100 years that most sophisticated and complex of vehicles, the aircraft, has been controlled and navigated by a human operator. The human crew has interpreted sensations of movement and the perceived patterns of visual information provided by the view of the world outside the aircraft or by the instruments within the cockpit.

Mention has already been made of the essential need to keep the human crew of an aircraft fully aware of what is happening outside the aircraft as well as inside. Situation awareness is already an important part of the control interface in the cockpit. In the future it will be of even greater importance because of the complexity and speed of a future war. It will also be important because of the need to make the most effective use of what will be extremely costly aircraft. To lose an aircraft because the pilot was not fully aware of what was happening must be avoided at all cost; 'cost' being the key word.

Whenever the design of the control system of a future high performance, agile, aircraft is contemplated the designer is faced with the 'human barrier'. As with the 'sound barrier', conditions on one side are different from those on the other. The 'human barrier' can be described in general terms in relation to aircraft cost and human resistance to abnormal environments. Cost is, of course, related to aircraft systems complexity and number. Simply stated: there comes a point at which the cost of providing a cockpit and interface for a human crew member is unacceptable. Of course, there is also the question of human pilot training costs and the alternative philosophy which favours uninhabited aircraft so as to avoid the loss of human lives.

Assuming that a human pilot is still one of the best all-round, versatile and flexible computers, then provision is still being made for a cockpit in many of the aircraft projected for the future. One air force in particular, the RAF, was in no doubt in 1997 that a human crew was best. There is general agreement among the different design offices that the future cockpit must meet the following requirements: (a) it must provide an information and control interface between pilot and aircraft so that the latter will respond unerringly to voice commands and to head/eye motion signals; (b) there has to be a two-way interchange of visual and aural information between pilot and machine so that controls and weapon systems can be selected and operated.

It is a fundamental fact of human progress in technology, if not in other activities, that we cannot abstract the future with any certainty from the past. However, with no other basis on which to predict the future, than when 'crystal ball' gazing we may have to use examples of past progress as a guide. The cockpit designer also has to anticipate future technologies in order to avoid a finished design being overtaken by events. It may take ten years or more to progress from first concept to an aircraft entering squadron service. In that time technology can advance at a rapid pace.

Particular cockpits for particular aircraft

In Europe and America design teams are involved with the cockpits for the Future Offensive Aircraft (FOA) and the Joint Strike Fighter (JSF). The EF2000 Eurofighter, which is similar in performance to the F-22, is already in production and has a cockpit, as described in chapter 6, which incorporates much of the thinking for the future.

The FOA for the RAF has a development target programme for entering squadron service in about 2018. A key factor is the air force's requirement that once the FOA is in service it must retain its potential as a weapon system until at least 2050. (The F-4 Phantom has been in service for nearly 40 years.) Such a requirement places an onerous task on the designers who must specify systems and cockpit interface equipment that will adapt easily to changes in the overall operational requirements. We have seen how in the past aircraft types that have started their service lives as, say, a high altitude interceptor have had to be modified to take on the role of a low-level attack. In the decades when such changes could be accommodated by a different version of the basic engine and a number of 'bolt on' systems, an aircraft could be adapted comparatively easily to such a new role. Even the cockpit and its interface usually needed only a few small changes to switches and weapon control and aiming system so as fit a new operational requirement. This frequently no longer applies because the systems of modern and future aircraft will be integrated to an even greater degree: change one thing and you change the lot.

We have already seen how the canopy shape of the F-117 is made up of straight line edges meeting at a point. This was done to alter the aircraft's radar signature so as to make it less observable by electronic sensing systems. Large 'bubble' canopies, even with a reflective film, cannot prevent some radar energy from entering into the large cavity of the cockpit and being reflected. If human pilots and a cockpit with transparencies are specified for future penetration attack aircraft the canopy or its equivalent will have to avoid acting as a reflector of radar energy. In general the fighter aircraft being projected for the future have none or very few excrescences. These are designs intended to make the aircraft invisible to all forms of detection and therefore permit only a cockpit which is completely buried within the airframe. Among the options for accommodating a human crew are: a virtual reality interface, an interface with indirect external vision using television and IR, and a variable geometry cockpit providing direct vision for low speed flight.

Some of the present generation of fighter/attack aircraft are equipped with sensors and systems which allow the pilot to detect, track and engage different types of target simultaneously. The combination of radar, infrared search and track and other avionics also copes with targets which are widely dispersed: some at high altitude, some over the horizon and others on the ground. Future aircraft will have even more versatile sensor and target acquisition systems. Presenting such a wide span of information in a way which does not overload and confuse the pilot is a major problem which has to be solved.

Future fighter/attack cockpits are being designed to take account of the limited abilities both physical and mental of a human pilot. These abilities vary in response to workload. There is the limit to the number of different mental and physical actions that can be undertaken simultaneously. This aspect of the human component of the information and control interface is of even greater importance for the future. To avoid overloading the pilot's abilities the interface has to be designed to present information to the pilot unambiguously and at the same time without cluttering up the visual task with 'not needed at the moment' information. The tactile elements in the cockpit must be designed for easy operation and accurate selection even during extreme environmental conditions such as high-G. The loads imposed on the human pilot during combat in a high-agility fighter can preclude the use of the hands for tactile inputs and therefore as many as possible of the aircraft's systems must have built-in intelligence so that they can operate for the greater part of the time automatically.

Another important design factor and one which has come to prominence in recent years is the proliferation of equipment 'mounted' on the pilot. Apart from helmet-mounted sights and communications equipment, environmental protection and safety devices festoon the pilot's body. Of course, some of this equipment is for providing protection in the event that the pilot has to eject. An important design target for the future has to be a reduction in the amount and volume of this equipment. Although the comfort of flying in shirt sleeves may not be practicable nevertheless it provides a useful target at which to aim when designing flying clothing and protection equipment.

Super agility

Mention has been made of aircraft with thrust vectoring which enables them to be flown at extreme angles of attack, at an angle to the horizontal flight path and to perform super agile manoeuvres. In 1994 a modified F-16D gave a window onto flight control in the future. Thrust vectoring of the F-16D was simultaneously controlled by the digital engine control system and the flight control system. No longer were the primary flight controls of roll, yaw and pitch operated independently of thrust control. The F-16D took the 1960s generation Harrier vectoring thrust control a significant way forward and showed the way in which fighter/attack controls may develop. The new concept required additional controls in the cockpit. Extra switches were added to the basic HOTAS layout. These enabled the pilot to vary the rate at which pitch, roll and yaw control was exercised. The angle-of-attack display on the HUD was expanded to match the aircraft's ability to achieve extreme angles.[1]

Human limits

The performance of super agile fighter/attack aircraft is already ahead of the physical limitations of the human body. Pilots are tested in centrifuges to determine the G level at which they black out. Among the results of these tests is the observation that short pilots, particularly females, can better resist the adverse effects of high G. Tall pilots are at a disadvantage because the heart has to pump blood over a greater distance. Aeromedical establishments teach breathing and muscular control techniques in order to raise a pilot's G level tolerance. Among the limitations of the human pilot related to high G effects is that of the neck muscles. These have to support and hold in position a head which on average weighs 18 lb. To this must be added a helmet weight of, say, 5 lb. The total weight on the pilot's neck has to be multiplied by the value of G. At only 4 G it becomes 92 lb. When G levels as high as seven are being considered then the load on the neck becomes unsustainable. Even Formula One racing drivers have to use head restraint to resist the sideways force during cornering and then we are only talking about three to four G. Therefore we

are up against the conflict between completely restraining the head and limiting the use of head-pointing systems and 'eyeball' searching.

Aircraft could be developed in the future which are not only agile in the present meaning of the word but also able to accelerate and manoeuvre to a degree which will be completely unacceptable to the human body. Even the scientists studying future space travel to other galaxies are already warning that to travel such immense distances in a life time will impose acceleration forces far outside those sustainable by the human body, let alone a space craft's structure. In this connection research into eliminating G effects on the human body form an important goal for scientists. Once again, the cockpit as we now know it may be used only for the comparatively more sedate craft in low orbit round the earth.

Crew comfort

Reference has been made to the ill effects of noise and vibration on the occupants of a cockpit. For example, acoustic noise can affect an aircrew member in a number of ways. It interferes with communication both between crew members and with external voice links. Noise is a significant contributor to fatigue because excessive exposure tends to reduce levels of awareness. The medical effects can lead to hearing damage as experienced by some musicians performing works requiring extremely high noise levels.

There are two basic ways of attenuating the adverse effects of acoustic noise. One, classified as passive attenuation. The other, as active cancellation. The former arrived in WWI in the shape of a close-fitting helmet with pads over the headphones and ears. A modern passive attenuation helmet keeps acoustic noise to an acceptable level in the frequency band of about 200 Hz to 1 kHz. (Concert Pitch A, above middle C, is 440 Hz.) Outside this band it is difficult to suppress noise, even with many layers of sound absorbing and deflecting barriers.

Active cancellation uses destructive interference whereby sound is cancelled by electronically adding a similar sound which is 180° out of phase. An electro-acoustic system generates the out-of-phase cancelling sound. However, even with the most sophisticated electronic circuitry effective cancellation is confined to those frequencies below 2 kHz.[2]

Future requirements

As with current cockpit design processes , the future fighting cockpit starts with five major requirements: the operational role, the flight envelope, the weapon system, aircraft and human protection and the total information environment

One way to approach the subject of the future cockpit is to consider the aerospace technologies being studied at present. Many of the ideas under consideration or evaluation will have an effect on the cockpit and its human occupant. The design requirements for the cockpit of the future can be considered in relation to the following typical pilot demands and questions:

(a) 'I want to be at 50,000 feet at time 2010 over position X'

(b) 'I want the weapons system to fire at the target at two o'clock high'

(c) 'I want option C' (The avionics having offered a number of different courses of action).

The design of a future fighter/attack cockpit has to be based on the information and outputs of the control interface of which the pilot is an integral part. The pilot can receive information from the real world seen through the cockpit transparencies, from analogues of the real world provided by instruments and displays, from aural signals and, possibly, from a virtual reality world. The pilot is also provided with information in the form of physical sensations associated with aircraft movement and accelerations. The pilot's inputs to the aircraft as a weapon system include: head and eye pointing, tactile selection and movements using hands and feet as well as voice and, possibly, thoughts.

It is neither easy or wise to attempt to predict the extent to which the cockpit of the future will incorporate techniques that at present are only at the experimental stage. As it is, virtual reality and remote control in themselves are already two techniques that could directly affect the design of the cockpit: the latter, of course, eliminates the need for a control and information interface because the present-day cockpit is only there to accommodate the human crew.

The principal design target for the cockpit of the future, as envisaged at present, is that of optimum interaction between pilot and aircraft. In other words, the aircraft's information systems must not only 'talk' to each other without ambiguity and loss of data, but must also clearly and precisely keep the human element of the cockpit aware fully of what is happening to the aircraft, both as a vehicle and as a weapon system. There must be no errors on the part of the pilot induced by the machine. In this respect the human pilot has to be considered in terms of bionics with his or her mental and physical abilities matched to those of the aircraft. This set of desirable criteria was also applicable to the design of all cockpits in the past; including those of 1914. But, of course, neither the technologies nor a comprehensive understanding of human factors were available in the earlier decades of powered flight.

The fighter/attack cockpit

Before considering some of the potential features of the cockpit and its equipment for the future the following decision by the USAF in 1996 is appropriate to the subject:

The USAF is changing its thinking from how many aircraft it will take to destroy one target, to how many targets can be destroyed by one aircraft.

This statement sets out one of the most important overall cockpit design requirements. It emphasises the required multi-role capability which in turn leads to the complexity required for an aircraft able to take on, sometimes simultaneously, more than one target during a sortie. This complexity has a direct effect on the cockpit and its equipment. The air forces of the global powers are no longer interested in the un-sophisticated aircraft. Cockpit design has come a long way away from, for example, the Folland Gnat lightweight fighter of the 1950s. The coming generation of fighter/attack aircraft will participate in a war planned to last no more than a few days. A war in which the maximum number of enemy targets are 'taken out' in the first day and both airborne and ground resources of the enemy are effectively eliminated. Such a war scenario demands expensive and complex aircraft which in turn demand the most efficient human-machine interface design in the cockpit as possible.

The avionic and sensor systems of the future fighter/attack aircraft will provide 100 times, perhaps even more, information than those of the 1990s. In contrast the human crew member of the future is unlikely to have any increase in mental ability over those of today's aircrew. This fact introduces a particular key cockpit system requirement: namely, that any advances, such as computing power, in the information/control interface must recognise that the mental performance of its human component has not increased at the same rate as technology.

When events occur at a rate greater than those to which the pilot can respond there is a serious problem. In practice the human mentally 'switches off' attention to some of the tasks. Then the performance of the overall control interface in the cockpit, of which the human is an integral part, will deteriorate. To compensate for the difference in performance between the system and the human, the latter can be helped by simplifying individual tasks, by providing unambiguous and easily understood information displays, by uncomplicated controls and by greater use of automatic systems and AI.

The view ahead

Increasingly we are being faced with the possibility of abandoning our present convention that the pilot's vision, directly or indirectly, of the world outside is from an eye-point within the aircraft. A remote eye-point, or 'fly-on-the-wall', position may be preferable. This type of display is used in arcade flight and car racing games.

Future manned aircraft will most likely include specialised types able to take off and land vertically, hover and move in any direction and not necessarily pointing in the direction of flight. This omni-directional ability is in conflict with the present convention that the pilot faces toward the front of an aircraft and is able to see directly over the generally forward arcs of vision. This suggests that all-round, including above and below, visual arcs will have to be provided using imaging sensor electronics. These will present their visual information on the helmet visor or directly on to the pilot's retinas.

A multi-camera TV, with LLTV, and IR, systems could, for example, provide omni-directional viewing when an aircraft is operating in proximity to the ground or other aircraft, friendly or otherwise. However, when we consider the cockpit of hypersonic aircraft the G forces will impose a restricted posture on the human pilot which in turn will restrict the arcs of view obtained by head movement, or alternatively the human component may restrict the agility of the machine. Aerodynamic considerations and protection against harmful radiation, such as lasers, may mean that direct vision transparencies for the human operator may not be practicable. A possible line of development is the variable geometry cockpit which can adapt to a particular phase of flight. The civil Concorde is an example of a 'two phase' cockpit.

The aerodynamic characteristics of future aircraft, particularly of agile high performance types, may limit direct control by a human pilot. The pilot, in the outer control loop, may be concerned only with simple commands such as 'start', 'go to', 'intercept X' and 'search for'.

A real or virtual view?

During the past seventy years the quantity and quality of information, in the form of instrument displays, has steadily improved. The improvements have been absolutely necessary in order that aircraft in general can achieve increased performance and versatility. The combination of the digital computer, databuses, electronic displays and electronic sensors has given us a virtually real view of the world outside the aircraft irrespective of the quality of the visibility.

Experiments have demonstrated how the human pilot can be virtually independent of direct vision of the real world.

In 1995 NASA initiated a civil flight deck research programme, some of the results of which were applicable to the military aircraft cockpit. A complete aircraft flight deck was enclosed within the fuselage of a Boeing 737. The test pilots controlled the aircraft in all phases of flight, including landing, using a closed circuit TV which provided a view ahead. A safety crew occupied the normal cockpit in the nose of the 737. The object of the test flights was to evaluate a cockpit having no direct external view of the real world outside the aircraft. Supersonic transports of the future are being considered with optimum nose shapes related to aerodynamic factors which will not permit the discontinuity of a windscreen.

The fighter/attack cockpit of the future may be designed primarily around the concept of 'virtual reality'. This is a cockpit in which all information is synthetic in origin and computer generated. The pilot will derive an entire view of the outside world from information provided by electronic sensors including radar, low-light TV and millimetric infra-red techniques. The electronic sensors combined with powerful computers can provide the pilot with an enhanced view of what is going on both inside and outside the cockpit. The pilot's arcs of vision will no longer be limited; views directly astern or underneath the aircraft will be available.

A key feature of the virtual reality cockpit will be the pilot's helmet visor. This becomes the primary visual information display. With a helmet projection system, information gathered and processed from FLIR, LLTV, GPS, inertial navigation systems and the databases of the aircraft's computers will be projected onto the visor or directly onto the retinas of the pilot's eyes using a virtual retinal display (VRD). In the virtual reality cockpit the pilot will look and talk and virtually touch in order to select a position in space or on the map or an aircraft system. Whether primary control of the aircraft's ability to roll, pitch, yaw or crab is entrusted to look and voice alone is another matter. It will need far more research before the answer is known.

A virtual reality system eliminates the need for conventional fenestration. This has three major advantages: one, it simplifies the design of the cockpit; two, it protects the pilot against adverse radiation and, three, it avoids the aerodynamic penalty of a cockpit whose shape usually interrupts the ideal aerodynamic lines of an aircraft and is a surface whose geometry may not be in accord with the requirements of stealth.

Thrust integrated with flight control

The designs for agile, variable-geometry STOVL fighters, with dirigible nozzles being studied raise the question of how many primary flight and thrust control levers? For example, the Harrier AV-8B has three primary inceptors (levers): longitudinal thrust (throttle), thrust vector (nozzle position) and the three-axis central control stick. [An 'inceptor' is a term used for describing an input device, such as a lever, used by a pilot to control a system and is therefore the opposite to a receptor.][3]

A UK MoD research programme VAAC (Vectored thrust Aircraft Advanced flight Control) studied different methods of controlling a STOVL. One was a two-inceptor system: one for longitudinal velocity and the other for flight path control. The left hand controlled longitudinal velocity. Although it acted like a throttle it did not directly control engine thrust because engine power needed to be high during hover as well as at wing-borne, high speed, flight. At the lower end of the speed range the left hand inceptor controlled speed on the ground and in hover and then blended into acting as a conventional throttle as the aircraft accelerated away from the hover mode. Another system studied had a thumb wheel at the top of the stick for speed control.

For over 90 years the pilot's leg and feet muscles have been used to effect yaw control. In the future the primary control of an aircraft may be very different because yaw control will be even further integrated with roll and pitch. The feet might be used, as an example, to control the thrust vector.[4]

Too much information

Mention has already been made of the 'embarrassment of riches' which have confronted aircrew in the last three decades. Too much information can increase not decrease workload. With so much information generated both by an aircraft's own systems and by sensors of information external to an aircraft, the crew can be confused and unable to sort out the necessary from the unnecessary. The key factor in the military combat aircraft cockpit is that of time.

Given plenty of time and a pencil and paper the crew can sort out and allocate priorities among many items of information. But, of course, the cockpit environment is usually one in which the crew has to react in milliseconds to events. The single-seat pilot is particularly vulnerable when it comes to an abundance of information. This is one of the reasons why some air forces prefer a two-seat cockpit for combat aircraft so that tasks can be shared.

The '*need to know*' is one criterion for discriminating among different data. Another is '*knowing is not much good if nothing can be done about it*'. The first encourages the design of the 'dark' cockpit in which information is only displayed or announced for those systems relevant to a particular phase of flight and which have failed or are about to fail. A mass of green lights and a string of verbal 'OKs' do not enhance situation awareness.

Artificial intelligence (AI), as discussed in the previous chapter, is rapidly becoming an understood technology and it is certain to find even greater application in the future. With AI as a foundation, mission management systems (MMSs) are being developed which focus the crew's attention on what is essential to know at any particular moment or phase of flight. The electrical power management system (EPMS) is an example of a system within a hierarchy of Intelligent Vehicle Management System (IVMS) elements. IVMS embraces many aircraft systems for the future and particularly for those which interface with a human crew. Another element is the Central Warning System (CWS) which sorts, weights and presents warnings and advice in such as way as to avoid increasing crew workload.

Keeping the pilot in the information loop and ensuring good SA was one of the more important design targets set by Saab for the JAS39 Gripen. The Swedish Air Force 2000 concept integrates with the Gripen cockpit a number of different information sensor systems: such as signal intelligence (SIGINT) and airborne early warning (AEW) and the ground-based information and control centres. The concept also links each aircraft with others in the formation or in the area of operations. The electronic displays in the cockpit ensure that the pilot is fully aware of the complete tactical situation. Even when the Gripen is on the ground awaiting a 'scramble' order or about to turn onto the runway, the pilot can view the latest tactical information.

Head and eye control

Using head movement to control pitch, yaw and roll is a concept introduced in the 1960s.[5] Although there are few electro-mechanical or electronic problems in devising such a system there are undoubtedly limitations for military applications; at least some of which would weigh against it being developed. One disadvantage would be the need to restrain the pilot's head in such a way that the only head movements allowed would be those for controlling the aircraft's trajectory.

It would be most unwise to predict that 'head' control will never be used. However, the trend at present is the development of combined head and eye movements to 'point' to desired ground features, targets and to elements of the cockpit interface.

As noted in the previous chapter, HMD-pointing has been demonstrated as a non-tactile, i.e. without the use of the pilot's extremities, method of controlling an aircraft's weapon-system. This has been achieved without the need for the pilot to keep the head in one position. The pilot looks at a position in three-dimensional space and confirms that what he or she is looking at is the desired position or target to which the aircraft must be directed. The key to all this is the computer which is able to sense eye-movements. Eventually the present technologies will be advanced to a level at which the computer systems detect eye-pointing movements and smoothly control the aircraft without subjecting it to unacceptably excessive G loads. This is, after all, only an extension of the system whereby the pilot controls the aircraft using hands and feet in response to 'director' symbology on the HUD or HMD or even on the RIS.

However, it is a case of 'possible' rather then 'when' before direct control by eye-pointing is perfected because the accurate measurement of eye position is a very difficult task compared with detecting head position.

Full-authority Direct Voice Input

As described in the previous chapter DVI can be used for commands and questions. It has been suggested that eventually it could be used for aerodynamic/thrust control. Control about the three axes of roll, pitch and yaw as well as thrust vectoring requires co-ordination, whether by a computer or by a human pilot. It is a task in which information from a number of sensors, either artificial or human, is processed and acted upon simultaneously to provide the desired integrated control of the aircraft's movements. 'Simultaneously' is the key word. DVI has the disadvantage that the commands, such as 'Roll fifteen degrees and dive ten degrees' is a mouthful which takes far too long compared with the reaction times of the sensory and nervous systems of man or computer: even the former can react in hundredths of a second. The above voice command takes at least five seconds. That may be acceptable for a slow responding big transport aircraft but not for an agile fighter/attack aircraft Therefore within our present knowledge it is difficult to visualise the use of DVI for flight control during a 'missile fight' using vectored thrust.

Although at this time the next generation of combat aircraft are envisioned as entering service between 2010 and 2020 those charged with thinking about the future try to think as much as forty years ahead. For example the USAF has had a series of 'future' programmes projected thirty years ahead. In the USA there have always been a number of 'black' projects. These are subject to extreme security and are funded separately from other defence budgets. In other countries there are 'black' projects but these are subject to even greater secrecy than those of the USA. Among the more important goals of the 'black' projects are the hypersonic (Mach 5 to 25) aircraft. Aircraft within this category have to perform both as present 'conventional' types and as spacecraft able to orbit the earth.

As this book was being printed scientists, researchers and development engineers were devising revolutionary interface concepts of outstanding ability; including extending the use of DVI.

Future complications

This book is not intended to cover the cockpits and controls of rotary wing aircraft. However alternative methods of producing lift and forward propulsion now being developed will require a combination of helicopter and fixed-wing flight controls. The controls for these new types of air vehicle are significantly different from those of conventional fixed-wing aircraft; including those which are able to make short take-offs and vertical landings. They require two sets of flight controls; one for vertical flight and the other for wing-borne flight. Because of the need to simplify the pilot's task a control system is needed which ensures safe transition from vertical to wing-borne flight and vice versa. They have to be fully 'fly-by-wire'. Had the digital computer and fly-by-wire technologies not been developed it is unlikely that designers and test pilots would have ventured into this particular arena of future flight.

Virtual design

On the subject of virtual reality, this technique is already being used in the design of the human/machine interface. In the 21st century it will be the principal design decision-making tool. The complex interactions between the many different specialists involved with cockpit design will be simplified and decisions reached more quickly by applying virtual reality.

Advanced visualisation techniques based on virtual reality enable design progress to be monitored with fewer opportunities for mistakes. The cockpit for example can be visualised not just on a computer screen but through the visual input units worn by the designers. It can be viewed from any angle and equipment can be moved around and conflicts instantly resolved. Using linked computer systems designers located remotely from each other can view and interact with a common visualisation. They can individually move, insert or eliminate features. The ergonomists can virtually move the extremities and head of an anthropometric 'dummy' to check arcs of vision, reach and all aspects of the pilot's ergosphere.

175

Simulation

Simulation will contribute even more to the training and re-training of aircrew in the future. Simulators range from 'fixed-base' types used by aircrew to practise flight and cockpit procedures to the three-axis, full motion types. At present the world's major air forces depend very much on realistic flight simulators to keep down costs. Each year the flight simulator specialists introduce better visual interfaces. The range of simulated techniques is extended as more powerful and faster computers are incorporated.

We already have the multi-aircraft simulator in which air-to-air combat techniques can be rehearsed by two or more pilots each in a separate cockpit and each seeing a common simulated airspace and the other aircraft. However if the pilot pulls a 9 G turn the sky, the landscape and the flight instruments respond and the pilot senses the simulated control loads through the hands. But an important sensation is missing. This is the effect of G. It is possible to simulate to some degree the G effects by using inflatable airbags against the pilot's body. However this is nothing like the real thing and in particular the pilot's cardiovascular system is unaffected and there is no G-LOC. Therefore the simulator specialists now have realistically simulated G effects as a design target.

UAV (Unoccupied Aerial Vehicle)

The UAV makes no demand on the designer for a control interface, life-support and life-saving systems. Without a cockpit, within the generally accepted definition, the vehicle costs are reduced considerably.

The design of a remote control position also requires attention to detail and to achieving an efficient and effective control interface. However, the absence of complex health and safety systems for the human operator significantly reduces the number of design problems. And, the designer can programme the controlled vehicle to perform agile manoeuvres at Gs up to the vehicle's structural limits. But, a remote control station in which the operator has no sensory feed back of what the vehicle is doing could lead to the reduction of situational awareness. Piloting the tailless

NASA/Boeing X-36 UAV highlighted a number of 'remote' cockpit factors. The test programme emphasised the importance of having a well designed ground-based cockpit because the pilot did not have the kinematic cues, i.e. aircraft movement and accelerations, of a normal aircraft. The pilot in the remote cockpit was deprived of sounds and peripheral vision as well as acceleration effects imposed on the human body. This may mean that a sophisticated virtual reality control position has to be used which 'projects' the operator into the remote vehicle and which simulates acceleration effects.

A control interface for a UAV presents few hardware problems compared with the physiological and psychological considerations of a manned aircraft cockpit. Although a simplistic concept, a remote operator cannot endanger his or her life either by carelessness or a 'do or die' attitude when controlling a UAV which may be thousands of miles away. Therefore, careful thought has to be given to the way in which a human operator i.e. 'pilot', at the control station reacts to events. Obviously they must not treat it as if it were an arcade computer game.

In 1996 the UAV Dark Star programme in the USA suffered a number of take-off accidents because the flight control computer had not been programmed to handle 'wheelbarrowing' during the take-off run. When the main wheels left the runway before the nosewheel the resulting 'wheelbarrow' attitude induced vertical oscillations which the computer was unable to eliminate. The 'post mortem' raised the question of should a human pilot be included during proving flights? To include a human pilot would mean a complete redesign of the structure as well as the provision of controls, instruments and life support systems. It would also require a more comprehensive certification programme to cover the human factors such as the safe recovery of the crew in the event of a failure.

The pace of change in technology usually advances more quickly than expected. What can be predicted with some certainty, based on the technology of the 1990s, is the greater use of aircraft having no human crew and therefore the cockpit, as we now know it for military aircraft may be consigned to history.

We have already seen the effective use of uninhabited aircraft. These were the Tomahawk cruise missiles whose computers were programmed and up-dated throughout their flight by electronic reference to topographical features. They were used to destroy key Iraqi installations during the Gulf War of 1990–1. They and their later versions are certain to be used in wars to avoid the loss of human, expensive to train and expensive to protect, pilots. One thing is likely to remain a fundamental element of the design of future aircraft. This is the fact that a human, when compared with the machine, is a much better sensor and processor of information. That is providing there is not too much.

In the airwars of the past fifteen years increasing use has been made of airborne information gathering, processing and distributing command centres. These large aircraft, such as modified Boeing 747s, carry an extensive array of sensors and information processors which provide the operations staff on board with a 'global' view of the theatre of operations. Data is analysed and commands relayed to aircraft, ships and ground forces.

A forecast of future airwars includes large flying operations centres each accompanied by a host of smaller aircraft. Some could be drones; aircraft which accompany the 'mother ship'.[6] Some of the drones will carry sensors so that a clear picture of the target is transmitted back to the command aircraft. Others may be decoys; others, carrying maximum effect weapons, will be sacrificial and others will be suppressers of the enemy's defensive system. The command aircraft will keep well away, over the horizon (OTH) if need be, from a target. The human crew will have adequate sensing and weapon control systems, including the remotely controlled drones of the swarm, to destroy a target without exposing themselves to the enemy's lethal retaliatory weapons. Such a scenario suggests the development of attack aircraft which can be adapted on the flight-line to either have an inhabited cockpit or the space allocated to more sensor and weapon systems avionics.

Crew safety

In earlier chapters the ejection seat has been described along with the vital role it plays in helping to recover expensive-to-train aircrew in the event of trouble and its morale boosting role.

In the late 1990s some air forces studied the requirements for extending the range of body sizes and weights to be accommodated by an ejection seat. Previously seat performance was tuned to a limited range of pilot size. One of the reasons for a rethink about seat performance came with increasing pressure from the PC lobby to recruit female aircrew, particularly pilots.

One of the values used for calculating seat performance is the unclothed weight of a subject. Extending the weight range down to about 100 pounds and upward to 200 pounds became the design requirement. Although body weight became important in relation to seat dynamics, such as accelerations imposed on the pilot, it happened that during the 80s and 90s there was a proliferation of equipment strapped on to aircrew. So much so that the lighter weight of some aircrew, such as females, was compensated for by the increase in protective clothing, helmet with NVG and HMD, and other body mounted systems. However, the main problem came with those aircrew who were at the upper end of the weight limit range. Here the heavier equipment weight came close to or exceeded that for which the escape system had been designed originally.

The Martin-Baker ejection seats for the USN, the Eurofighter 2000, Rafaele and JPATS compensate for variations in 'naked' aircrew weight so that the lighter crew, such as females, are not subjected to excessive acceleration. At the other end of the weight scale these seats produce greater ejection thrust. Of course it is not only the ejection thrust that can adversely affect the human body, there is the severe deceleration as the parachute deploys. This may result in severe whiplash injuries to the smaller and lighter aircrew. Another consideration, related to the upper end of the weight range, is the risk of damage to the main parachute as it deploys.

Another aspect of crew survival techniques which may become of increasing importance is ejection seats for future aircraft which take off and land in a vertical attitude: as demonstrated for example by the Convair XFY-1. In effect, the seat will have to be ejected parallel to the ground and then vertically so as to gain sufficient height for parachute deployment.

Thinking about control

As for thought control, this is a technique which is going to need a lot more 'thought' before we can be certain of the role it might perform in the control interface. For example, thought control is being investigated seriously for use in the cockpit. Experiments have already been conducted which verify, albeit crudely, the basic principles. In 1996, for example, a severely paralysed man had electrodes implanted into the motor cortex of his brain. The detected brain signals were connected to a computer so that the patient could move the cursor and select functions. An alternative approach to thought control, investigated at the same time, used a finger stall sensor of the wearer's thoughts. This detected brain signals transmitted through the skin.

Possibly in two or three generations of aircraft ahead, i.e. about sixty years, thought control might be a usable science. Even though the aircraft control computers can be programmed to reject all but the acceptable commands, so as to eliminate catastrophic thoughts, this still imposes a fearsome discipline on the part of the human pilot. If, as may happen, thought control is perfected it may be so constrained in application that it will not be worth the effort. When and if it is adopted as the primary human contact with the machine, the cockpit, as we now know it, will probably no longer be there.

In addition to thought control it is foreseeable that future aircraft will provide more than the customary 'feed back' of control forces. A concept being investigated is the 'tactile' aircraft. Smart structures and surfaces that sense aerodynamic loads, airflows and boundary layer conditions, angle-of-attack, airspeed and other air data will be processed by a powerful computer. The output signals of the computer will pass to an overall body garment so that the pilot actually 'feels' what the aircraft is doing in relation to the atmosphere. Given such a system a pilot will be able to 'fly like a bird'.

All this musing about the future suggests, without being too positive, that the cockpit of the future will consist of interface systems included on the basis of 'horses for courses'. For example, DVI may be restricted to commands and interrogations which if pronounced incorrectly or with the wrong syntax will not jeopardise the aircraft. Combined head and eye pointing using HMD or RIS will be used for controlling the aircraft as a weapon system and as a means of indicating to the computer systems the direction in which the weapon system is to be pointed; again the computers will eliminate any ambiguous or dangerous inputs. Eye-pointing is also important in those aircraft which are able to point the nose or weapon system at an angle to the aircraft's trajectory. For example future attack aircraft will be able to 'crab' along a line which is at an angle to the direct line to the target.

What all this may come down to by the year 2010 is the greater integration of the pilot into the total computer system as a sensory and information processor element of the aircraft. Somewhere in the world scientists are working on the ways of merging man and machine. The future may include 'plug-in' pilots which act as another computer but have no tactile link with the aircraft. They will be required to think, talk, see and listen but not to touch.

In other words, the pilot will be that part of the aircraft which at the end of a flight unplugs itself and walks away.

Notes

1. Gerzanics, M. (1994) paper presented at RAeS/AIAA/ITERA Test and Evaluation International Aerospace Forum 1994: *Aerospace* Sept 1994 edn. p. 34.
2. Gauger, D. *MILTECH* 5/95 edn. pp. 38–45.
3. *Aerospace*, Dec 1996 edn. pp. 10, 11.
4. Fitzpatrick, R.S. correspondence with author.
5. Melville Jones, G. Man-Machine Integration, *The Aeronautical Journal*, Vol. 72, 694, pp. 831 *et seq.*
6. Fitzpatrick, R.S. correspondence with author.

Selected Bibliography

Baker, W.J. (1970) *A History of the Marconi Co.* Methuen.

Blackett, P.M.S. (1962) *Studies of War.* Oliver & Boyd.

Bowen, E.G. (1987) *Radar Days.* Hilger.

Bowyer, M.J.F. (1984) *Interceptor Fighters for the Royal Air Force 1935–45.* Patrick Stephens.

Boyle, A. (1962) *Trenchard.* Collins.

Bridgeman & Stewart. (1938) *The Clouds Remember.* Gayle & Polden.

Brown, E. (1983) *Wings Of The Weird and Wonderful.* Airlife.

(1994) *Testing For Combat.* Airlife.

Bulmore, F.T.K. (1956) *The Dark Haven.* Cape.

Chapanis, A. (1965) *Research Techniques in Human Engineering.* Johns Hopkins.

Clarke, R.W. (1965) *Tizard.* Methuen.

Coombs, L.F.E. (1983) *Cockpits of the RAF.* Series in *Aeroplane Monthly.*

(1990) *The Aircraft Cockpit.* Patrick Stephens.

(1997) *The Lion Has Wings.* Airlife.

Curie, J. (1983) *Mosquito Victory.* Goodall.

Exupery, A. de St. (1939) *Wind Sand and Stars.* Heinemann.

Farley, J.F. *Modern Flight Instrument Displays As a Major Military Aviation Flight Safety Weakness.* AGARD Conference Proceedings No 347 (1983).

Flint, P. (1996) *Dowding and Headquarters Fighter Command.* Airlife.

Fredette, R. (1966) *The First Battle of Britain.* Cassell.

Frith, Group Captain N. (1994) *EF2000-Affordable Superiority.* RAeS lecture.

Goulding, J. (1986) *Interceptor.* Ian Allan.

Grennell-Milne, D. (1933) *Wind In The Wires.* Hurst & Blackett.

Gunston, W.T. (1990). *Avionics.* Patrick Stephens.

(1976) *Encyclopedia of Combat Aircraft.* Salamander.

(1976) *Night Fighters.* Patrick Stephens.

(1991) *Plane Speaking.* Patrick Stephens.

Harris, Sir Arthur. (1995) *Despatch On War Operations 23.2.42 to 8.5.45.* Cassell

Hartcup, G. (1970) *The Challenge of War.* David & Charles.

Her Majesty's Stationery Office. (1948) *Laboratory of the Air.*

Hinchliffe, P. (1996) *The Other Battle.* Airlife.

Hünecke, K. (1987) *Modern Combat Aircraft Design.* Airlife.

James, D. *Gloster Aircraft.* Putnam.

Jarrett, P. (1997) *Aircraft Of The Second World War.* Putnam.

Jewell, J. *Engineering For Life.* Martin-Baker.

King, H.F. (1971) *Armament of British Aircraft. 1909–1939.* Putnam.

Lewis, P. (1980) *The British Bomber Since 1914.* Putnam.

Lovell, Sir Bernard. (1991) *Echoes of War.* Hilger.

Mason, F.K. (1992) *The British Fighter.* Putnam.

(1994) *The British Bomber.* Putnam.

(1961) *Hawker Aircraft since 1920.* Putnam.

Middleton, D. (1985) *Test Pilots.* Guild Pub.

(1995) *Tests Of Character.* Airlife.

(1989) *Avionic Systems.* Longman.

Moore, W.G. (1963) *Early Bird.* Putnam.

Pallett, E.H.J. (1992) *Aircraft Instruments & Integrated Systems.* Longman.

Penrose, H. *The Great War and Armistice 1915–1919.* Putnam.

(1980) *The Ominous Skies.* RAF Museum.

Price, Dr A. (1973) *Aircraft Versus Submarine.* Kimber.

(1977 ed.). *Instruments of Darkness.* Macdonald & Janes.

(1995) *The Spitfire Story.* Arms & Armour.

Raleigh, Sir Walter. (1928) *The War in The Air.* Clarendon.

Rawnsley & Wright. (1957) *Night Fighter.* Collins.

Robinson, D.H. (1973) *The Dangerous Sky.* Foulis.

Satchell, P.M. (1973) *Cockpit Monitoring and Alerting Systems.* Ashgatex.

Saward, Group Captain D. (1959) *The Bomber's Eye.* Cassell.

(1984) *'Bomber' Harris.* Buchan & Enright.

Skorczewski, L. (1989) *Cockpit Requirements.* British Aerospace paper.

Terrain, J. (1985) *The Right of the Line.* Hodder & Stoughton.

Townsend, Group Captain P. (1970) *Duel of Eagles.* Weidenfeld & Nicolson.

Trenkle, F. (1958) *Bordfunkgerate der deutschen*

Luftwaffe 1935–45. Motorbuch Verlag.

Wallace Clarke, R. (1993) *British Aircraft Armament Vols 1 & 2* Patrick Stephens.

Wallace, G. (1957) *RAF Biggin Hill.* Putnam.

Wallace, G.F. (1972) *Guns of the Royal Air Force.* William Kimber.

Williams, T.I. (1978) *A History of Technology Vol VII Part II.* Oxford.

Wilson, Pam. (1996) *EF2000 Cockpit Design – The Development Process.* British Aerospace paper.

Wood & Dempster (1961) *The Narrow Margin.* Hutchinson.

Wooldridge, E.T. (1995) *Into The Jet Age.* Naval Institute Press.

Yeates, V.M. (1934) *Winged Victory.* Jonathan Cape.

Acronyms

A&AEE	Aeroplane & Armament Experimental Establishment
AFCS	Automatic Flight Control System
AEW	Airborne Early Warning
AIAH	Advanced Integrated Avionic Helmet
AI	Airborne Interception radar or Artificial Intelligence
AMLCD	Active Matrix Liquid Crystal Display
ASRAAM	Advanced Short Range Air-to-Air Missile
ASV	Air-to-Surface Vessel radar
BVR	Beyond Visual Range
CAD	Computer Aided Design
COMED	Combined Map and Electronic Display
CWS	Central Warning System
DVI	Direct Voice Input
ECM	Electronic Counter-Measures
EPMS	Electrical Power Management System
FADEC	Full Authority Electronic Engine Control
FLIR	Forward Looking Infra-Red
G	Acceleration due to gravity
G-Loc	G induced Loss Of Consciousness
GPS	Global Positioning System
HDD	Head-Down Display
HMD	Helmet-Mounted Display
IR	Infra-Red
IVMS	Intelligent Vehicle Management System
JPATS	Joint Primary Aircraft Training System
JSF	Joint Strike Fighter
JTIDS	Joint Tactical Information Distribution System
LLTV	Low Light TV
McDD	McDonnell Douglas
MDC	Miniature Detonation Cord
MHDD	Multi-function Head-Down Display
MMS	Mission Management System
NBC	Nuclear Biological and Chemical warfare
NVG	Night Vision Goggles
OTH	Over The Horizon
RIS	Retinal Imaging System
SA	Situation Awareness
SIGINT	Signals Intelligence
STOVL	Short Take Off and Vertical Landing
TIALD	Thermal Imaging Airborne Laser Designator
VAAC	Vectored thrust Aircraft Advanced flight Control
VIFF	Vectoring In Forward Flight
VRD	Virtual Retinal Display

Index